Easy story
to learn French
Good Reading!!
Justine

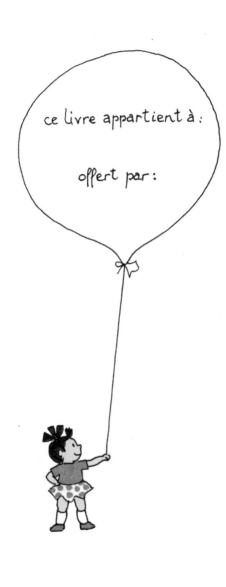

RETROUVEZ **mimi cracra** DANS

MA PREMIÈRE BIBLIOTHÈQUE ROSE

Agnès Rosenstiehl

Mimi Cracra
au bord de la mer

Pour Ella Choudhury,
ma petite-fille chérie qui n'a peur de rien !
A.R.

Hachette Livre, 43, quai de Grenelle, 75015 Paris.

Amuse-toi avec Mimi Cracra sur son site :
www.mimicracra.com

1

Le château
de sable

Ah, quelle chance ! c'est les vacances, mais... où est la mer ?

Moi, j'arrive, et la mer est partie ! Y a plus d'eau ! C'est pas possible, ça ! Où elle est, la mer ? Le sable ne va pas

partir, j'espère ? Mais, mais, où est la mer ? Ah ça y est ! Je la vois ! Eh bah dis donc, elle est loin, celle-là ! Mille kilomètres, je crois ! Pff ! Puisqu'il n'y a que du sable, il faut faire un château, si j'ai bien compris !

D'abord, moi j'enlève mes habits, et mes sandales. Oh là ! J'ai plein de sable dans mes sandales ! C'est doux, mais ça remplit trop mes doigts de pied, je trouve ! Bon, maintenant je voudrais bien me rappeler : y a qui dans ce sac ? Allez, sortez tous, on est arrivés !

Terminus, attention à la fermeture de la fermeture éclair, faut pas vous faire pincer ! Ah ah, mais j'ai emmené toute la classe, ma parole ! Nounours, je savais que tu étais là ! Mais tu as emmené Poupée ? T'es amoureux ou quoi ! Toi, Petit Cochon, sors de là, je t'ai vu, et quoi ? Hein ? Loup du Plastoc, ici ? Un

loup au bord de la mer ?
C'est interdit, je te préviens :
t'as pas intérêt à aboyer,
sinon le maître nageur te
dira de venir dans sa cabane

de police ! Hé hé, qui je vois là encore ? Assurbanipal... vieux canard, c'est de l'eau salée, la mer : je te préviens ! Tu feras mieux de ne pas en

boire, sinon t'auras du mal au ventre garanti ! Et un seau, et un camion, et une pelle, et une serviette, et des provisions pour faire manger tous les voyageurs...

Ouah, y a beaucoup de monde sur cette plage, on voit que c'est les vacances ! Vous allez tous m'aider à construire notre château d'amis, n'est-ce pas ? Je suppose, euh, ici : voici une très bonne place, avec beau paysage : on voit la mer très très loin, donc pas de danger de vagues. Viens voir m'aider, la pelle : on va préparer une tour pour mettre au milieu.

Faut bien tasser : tap tap tap ! Et après, jdoung : on

dépote et on soulève ! Hé ho, le camion, tu dois transporter du sable, ce sera nos murs. Très bien transporté. Mais y a pas de décorations, pas de porte. On va aller au marché aux puces avec Nounours ! Vous, vous restez là pour garder le château, et les outils, et le goûter. On revient dans un mois, Nounours et moi, parce que c'est un très grand marché aux puces, et c'est difficile de trouver les choses qu'on veut. En route, ce lointain voyage va rapporter beaucoup de marchandises. Bon salut.

2

Le marché
aux puces

Ah, quelle chance, c'est les vacances, on va au marché aux puces !

Nounours, attention, on arrive près de la jungle où il y a les puces de mer.

Eh, regarde : elles sautent

très haut !... Mais elles ne piquent pas : c'est ça l'avantage ! Elles adorent toute cette forêt d'algues, car il y a là tout ce qu'il faut pour elles là-dedans : des coquillages qui bâillent, des trucs que la mer donne à la plage, et même des bouts de bois de bateaux cassés...

Regarde bien tout ce qu'il y a là-dedans : pleins de trésors, je te garantis. Tiens, regarde ! Un bout de verre tout rond et lisse comme un caillou : ça nous fera une fenêtre pour le salon : hop dans le seau ! Et là : il y a des petits coquillages tout jaunes : très bien pour faire les lampes, d'accord ?

Et celui-là ! Énorme ! C'est la porte d'entrée de notre château ! Et cette planchette pour faire le pont devant l'entrée ! Et là, ho dis donc ! Une tong !... Abandonnée ! On la prend !

Ça, c'est quoi ? Une grosse ficelle : pas mal pour fermer l'entrée. Dis, il est vraiment génial, ce petit marché aux puces : bien mieux que les autres ; et en plus c'est gratuit, tu as remarqué ? Et au fait ! Les algues rondes, c'est super pour faire des plantes autour du château ! On en prend un kilo, d'accord ? Et tiens : des petits coquillages blancs. On dirait des volets, donc on les garde comme

volets ! Ouah, un très beau caillou ! Je le prends. Bouh, il est plein, le seau !

On rentre ! Nounours, ne traîne pas avec les puces de mer, moi je te le dis : elles vont te chatouiller !

Hé ho ! On arrive ! Fini les courses ! Et voilà, c'est complet : le château a toutes ses fenêtres et même un jardin autour de lui !

Ceux qui ont le droit d'y entrer s'appellent : Petit Cochon et Loup du Plastoc !

Allez-y, et ne faites pas de bêtises, car on vous voit très bien ! On est des géants et on voit tout ce qui se passe dans ce château : Nounours est le petit géant, et moi le gros !

Petit Cochon, toi tu restes en bas dans le jardin. Tu t'allonges, tu rêves et tu regardes le coucher de soleil qui n'est pas encore prêt. Attends patiemment. Et toi, Loup du Plastoc, tu montes en haut, avec tes dents de loup et tes habitudes féroces, pour que les ennemis n'entrent pas dans notre château. Interdit, compris ? Dans le jardin, j'enfonce le seau. Surprise rapide : ça

fait une piscine, pour quand
nous aurons de la pluie !…
J'espère qu'il y en aura un
jour. En attendant, c'est là
que va Poupée, car elle ne
sait pas où aller : elle est sans

abri, et le seau c'est son abri.

Tout ce travail est très fatigant, surtout avec la chaleur : je crève de chaud, moi !

D'ailleurs je vais organiser un peu de rafraîchissement : je vais aller me baigner dans la mer qui m'attend. Mon maillot de bain sera très content et moi aussi. Soyez parfaitement sages, et ne bougez pas de là pendant que je vais essayer la mer. Votre travail c'est de garder notre château. Bon, très très bien. Le camion est bien garé ? Dans une bonne place ? Gratuite en plus ? Eh bien j'y vais, et salut et à tout à l'heure !

3

La petite mare de mer

Ah, quelle chance, c'est les vacances, alors on court !

Hou là là là là ! C'est vraiment loin, et il fait vraiment très chaud, sur cette route ! Jamais on va arriver ! Ah ! Découverte d'explorateur !

Voici une petite mer vraiment géniale. Ho, comme elle est rafraîchissante ! Avec des petits cailloux dedans ! Et pas du tout profonde !

Ici, je peux baigner ma culotte de bain, je peux baigner mes jambes. On pourrait rester là toute la vie. En tout cas si j'étais un poisson, c'est ça que je ferais : j'habiterais ici, avec mon lit en petits cailloux et ma table en galet. Ha ! Mais il y en a un, de poisson ! Au secours !

Un vrai ! Bon, pas très dangereux, quand même. Tu m'as fait peur, toi ! Mais où il est, maintenant ? C'est dingue comme ça nage vite, un poisson ! Surtout celui-là ! Ah, le voilà qui revient. Il veut récupérer sa chambre, je pense... HA ! Quoi ? un petit crabe, maintenant ? Mais c'est fou ça ! Il va pincer mon poisson, celui-là !

Et il se cache dans les algues ! Ah le bandit, il veut attaquer mon poisson par surprise ! Mais mon poisson est caché derrière son petit rocher. Bon les gars, je vais me baigner dans la mer, car chez vous, il n'y a pas de vagues, malheureusement.

Je préfère les vagues. C'est loin encore, mais on voit très bien les vagues : assez petites. Y a qu'à courir, ça ira plus vite, ce voyage ! Tiens, une rivière, maintenant ? Bon je ne cours pas en traversant.

Rivière même pas profonde… Holà, un peu profonde, quand même ! Hé ho, ça descend ! Ah ah, ça y est, la montagne remonte ! Et voilà l'arrivée ! Y a plein de mousse, au bord de cette mer ! Hé ho, on dirait une machine à laver la vaisselle ! On aurait dû prendre toutes nos assiettes sales dans un panier à salade, et hop, c'est la mer qui fait la vaisselle ! Mais on ne les a pas prises donc tant pis pour nous.

Je vais me mouiller les pieds en premier, car c'est normal. Hou là ! Gla gla, gros gla gla gla, même ! Courage, Droipeton : c'est ton bain froid de pied, et Petongauche a encore plus

froid que toi, alors tu vois !
Hé là ! C'est quoi ça ! Une
vague qui me monte dessus !
Faut que je mette des petites
bouées, d'accord bon d'accord. Mais elles sont grosses,
ces petites vagues ! Plus
grosses qu'avant ou quoi ?

4

Faut boire
la tasse !

Ah, quelle chance, c'est les vacances, alors à l'eau !

Schlouff ! Pischouttt ! Ça y est mes cheveux sont tout mouillés : ah, ça rafraîchit ! Ouah c'est super, la mer, je le savais déjà, évidemment !

Hashglouglouglouglou…

Au secours, j'ai bu la tasse, elles sont folles, ces vagues !

Je vais au bord dans la mousse ! Attendez-moi, j'arrive, et je reviens, et je retourne, je tombe dans la vague erglouglouglou…

Glouglou… glouglou… très très salée, très trop salée !

Je fais gicler l'eau avec mes mains et hop ! Ça fait des diamants qui s'envolent ! Et hop, ça gicle jusqu'au ciel ! Et ça me fait un mouchoir

de mer : les tuyaux de mon nez sont tous lavés ! On dirait que je suis une petite sirène : mes pieds sont invisibles et j'ai une queue comme un poisson, et alors

je nage, comme un requin !
Non, pas un requin qui a
des dents dangereuses, mais
euh, un canard plutôt.

Et je flotte comme un
canard, parce que mes
petites bouées sont très
fortes !

Ça y est, y a encore une
vague qui me monte dessus,
gloups ! On dirait que ça
vous fait danser, la mer : on
danse tout seul, même si on
ne bouge pas, on danse
quand même : très com-

mode et même pas fatigant ! Moi je resterai là toute la vie ! Pourquoi est-ce qu'on me dit de sortir ?

J'ai même pas froid, d'abord ! Bon d'accord je sors, mais alors on va goûter ! Jdoung ! J'ai reçu une vague surprise qui me porte jusqu'au bord : taxi ! Automatique !

Mais ça me gratte ! J'ai plein de sable dans ma culotte ! Faut que je retourne, juste une seconde

pour laver mon sable, sinon dans ma culotte le sable va rester ! Et même j'enlève ma culotte pour la laver de son sable. Retourne dans la mer, le sable.

Et maintenant je peux la remettre, cette culotte de malheur ! Mais, ah c'est pas possible, ça !... J'ai encore plein de sable dedans : faut encore que j'aille me rincer car je ne peux pas marcher avec du sable dans ma culot-te ! Pfff... J'aimerais mieux être un singe qui n'a pas de culotte, ma parole ! Revoilà ma rivière, elle est plus grosse que tout à l'heure !

Mais dis donc ! J'espère que je peux passer, moi !

Hou là là là ! Profond comme un précipice ! Mais chaud comme un bain de maison ! C'est une rivière chaude !

Alors là, carrément génial ! Je flotte comme un bateau ! Tout mon sable est parti : c'est une rivière de rinçage.

Et voilà, de l'autre côté, le grand désert de sable qui recommence ! Et voilà ma petite mare, mais ! Elle est brûlante, celle-là ! Brûlante vraiment ! Je me demande si mon poisson est cuit là-

dedans, ou quoi ! Il a disparu ! Peut-être qu'il est tellement cuit qu'il est mort de chaud ; sauf s'il est dans les algues : au fait c'est peut-être lui qui a mangé le petit

crabe que je ne vois plus nulle part... ? Ah, les pauvres, par cette chaleur maritime, que vont-ils devenir ? Je reviendrai voir ça tout à l'heure. Pour le moment j'ai tellement faim de goûter que je peux courir sans m'arrêter jusqu'à mon château, là où sont nos provisions ! Hop, c'est la course !

Aïe aïe, je suis fatiguée de courir, mais aïe aïe, j'ai tellement faim que, aïe aïe, je cours à toute vitesse, mais aïe aïe, j'ai mal aux pieds de courir comme ça, mais vite car j'ai trop faim ! Ouf ! J'ai plein de sable collé sur moi ! Faut que je retourne à l'eau… Impossible : j'ai trop faim !

5

Bon goûter au château !

Ah, quelle chance, c'est les vacances, alors on mange !

Goûter sur le sable : sac de goûter, ouvre-toi ! Et hop, il s'ouvre ! Hum, ça sent la banane, là-dedans, hein ! De l'eau, vite ! Je meurs de soif

comme un explorateur ! Pas salée, j'espère ? De la salée, j'en ai bu plein, déjà ! J'en voudrais de la normale !

Ah, délice de la fontaine de la bouteille de la source merveilleuse ! Et banane excellente quand on revient de l'autre bout du monde, qui est la mer ! Et peau de banane qui va être enterrée dans la cave de notre château, par en dessous des algues ! Au fait, comment va-t-il, ce château ? Je crois que je vais terminer mon goûter au château !

J'emporte mes biscuits de mer et mon chocolat amer dans notre château.

Salut, mes amis !... C'est l'heure du festin et naturellement vous aurez votre festin aussi. Nounours, voilà ton papier de chocolat favori. Poupée, tu peux avoir un biscuit, puisque tu as été sage dans ton seau. Et vous les autres, je vous mets des petites assiettes en coquillages sur la terrasse de la tour, là où il y a le plus beau paysage. Et moi je m'installe dans la cour, où je peux mettre ma serviette pour m'asseoir dessus. Bon.

Fermez la bouche en mangeant. Compris ? Je vais vous raconter mon long voyage là-bas.

Écoute, Nounours. Je suis allée à l'aventure dans un

pays lointain. Au début, je vis un grand lac d'eau bouillante, où je rencontrai un poisson-chat qui devint mon ami. Hélas, un crabe géant le menaça. Mais je vins à son secours alors il put enfin s'échapper. Puis je sortis de l'eau bouillante, et je m'approchai d'une rivière très profonde, et ce fut obligatoire de la traverser, car c'était mon chemin d'aller par là, donc voilà. Ensuite j'arrivai au bord de l'Océan Fantastique, et je plongeai dans cet océan plein de vagues énormes qui m'attaquèrent avec leur mousse infernale et leur eau glacée ! Heureusement je mis mes bouées de sauvetage, et je fus sauvée du naufrage. Mais un sable empoisonné me piqua les fesses, et je pris ma culotte pour le chasser, alors il s'enfuit ! Je pus enfin sortir de cette mer gelée, mais une vague me poursuivit et me flanqua par terre sans me prévenir. Et comme je mourais de faim, je décidai de terminer mon aventure et de rentrer te retrouver pour tout te raconter. Tu as entendu

mon aventure, Nounours ?
Attends-moi, je vais voir s'il
n'y a pas un petit bonbon de
récompense pour nous. Et
voilà, il y en a un !

Mais que vois-je sur ton
pull ? Une puce de mer ?
Nounours, il faut la chasser,
sinon on va tous avoir des
puces ! Viens avec moi, on
va retourner au marché leur
rendre cette puce perdue...
Mais ho ho ho ! Il y en a
plein le fossé du château :
on dirait que c'est nos sol-

dats qui font de l'exercice, pour bien nous garder ! Toi, Nounours, tu es le chef des gardiens, et tu dois observer. Et qu'est-ce que tu vois ? Qu'est-ce qui se passe ?

6

La mer monte, monte, monte !

Ah, quelle chance, c'est les vacances, et la mer arrive !

Tu vois que la mer s'est rapprochée un petit peu : elle voyage vers nous, ma parole : et je vois qu'elle a même noyé ma rivière, çà alors : plus de rivière ! Tu vois ça, Nounours ?

Elle avance, la mer ! Il faut que nous défendions notre château ! Il faut que nous construisions un mur très haut, genre deux mètres. La pelle, vite. Toi, tu conduis le camion et tu lui montres où il faut mettre des tas de sable. Au travail, les gars, c'est la course ! Et hop, une tonne de sable qui arrive. Et attends, c'est pas fini du tout regarde : encore une tonne ! Ce camion a une force de Titan : un Titan, c'est le plus fort de tous. Et le gros mur est encore plus gros, et je vais chercher encore un biscuit car je suis

affamée par ces travaux ! La vieille tong ? Ce sera notre barque pour sauver Loup du Plastoc et Petit Cochon.

N'ayez pas peur, au château : nous avons entendu votre inquiétude et nous sommes les pompiers de secours.

Nounours, j'espère que tu es au courant : les pompiers, c'est pas seulement pour le feu : oui, c'est aussi pour les inondations ! Et pour tout, d'ailleurs ! Pour toutes les

catastrophes, les nucléaires, les pas nucléaires, et les normales. Je sens qu'il va y avoir une catastrophe, en tout cas, car je vois que la mer s'approche encore d'ici avec

audace, et qu'elle veut venir dans notre château. Mais notre mur est plus haut qu'elle et donc elle devra s'arrêter : obligée. On va renforcer notre mur avec tous nos bouts de bois.

Et qu'est-ce qu'on peut mettre encore ? Du sable, et toujours du sable ! Ma parole, Nounours, regarde ! La mer a encore avancé ! Elle court sur le désert de sable, alors tous ceux qui étaient sur ce désert ont les pieds mouillés et les voilà qui sont obligés d'enlever leurs chaussures, et d'ailleurs il faut qu'on mette toutes nos affaires sur le rocher derrière, sinon...

Je monte sur le rocher, et je te raconte : c'est l'Océan Fantastique qui monte, qui monte, qui monte encore ! Il arrive bientôt ici ! Et l'Océan Fantastique fait un bruit de tonnerre, avec des vagues énormes qui arrivent presque jusqu'à nous ! Il

mouille tout notre marché
aux puces, et je vois qu'elles
sont très contentes : elles
sautent et elles sautent dans
l'eau, elles remontent sur

le sable sec, et les algues pleines d'eau se mettent à flotter, et elles arrivent vers nous !

Elles se collent sur notre mur de sable et, aïe aïe aïe aïe, ça y est ! L'eau rentre dans notre fossé, autour de notre beau château fort pas très fort !

7

Catastrophe maritime !

Ah, quelle chance, c'est les vacances, et voilà une inondation !

Pourtant notre château ne s'écroule pas encore, pas du tout : la mer l'entoure, et moi je cours autour !

Montez sur votre tong de débarquement. Venez en direction du rocher de secours, car votre château est attaqué.

Attention, grimpez tous sur ce rocher qui est une immense montagne pour tous les naufragés, ceux du monde entier. C'est notre nouveau refuge : je vais vous installer et ne tombez pas. Restez sur le rocher, je vais voir ce qui se passe. Eh bien je vous préviens qu'il se passe que ça déborde ! Je creuse avec ma pelle pour faire de la place à l'Océan Fantastique mais il déborde quand même, splash ! aïe aïe aïe aïe, le mur s'écroule complètement ! Ça, c'est le début de notre catastrophe et, oh là là, notre tour glisse, et notre terrasse glisse...

Ah là là là, splash encore une vague pleine de puces de mer et finale de la finale ! Notre glorieux monument de château du prince de l'Océan Fantastique explose dans l'eau, et on ne voit plus rien du tout! Ben dis donc, il était pas très solide, je trouve ! Vite il faut sauver les meubles, dites donc : la

fenêtre en verre vert, ça nous fera un trésor d'avance pour notre coffre de pirate. Et un autre trésor : ce double coquillage attaché ! Qu'est-ce qu'il fait là ? Il vient d'arriver, tout neuf : c'est une moule !

Nounours, écoute : une moule de mer, ce n'est pas du tout comme un moule à sable, tu m'as comprise ! Cette moule... oh zut, cassé le petit élastique qui tient le couvercle, et je vois une

idée : on dira que c'est mon vernis à ongles violet ! Un peu trop grand, mais très beau quand même. Il m'en faut d'autres pour que mes pieds soient complets... Bof, rien dans ces nouvelles vagues, rien dans les ruines de cet ancien château de l'Antiquité, et rien du tout dans cette forêt d'algues qui bougent tout le temps...

Mais si ! Petite moule à bâbord ! Et là, ficelle en nylon pour aller à la pêche !

Et encore un truc, genre bouchon qui flotte : un flotteur, avec un trou : une bouée pour toi, Nounours ! Et pile à ta taille ! Nous sommes des naufragés sur notre île déserte !

8

Fin du
naufrage !

Ah, quelle chance, c'est les
vacances et on a fait naufrage !

Hé ho, au secours ! Hé ho,
au secours : la mer redes-
cend ! Elle s'en va !... Pas
gênée : elle casse notre châ-

teau et puis elle s'en va ! Regardez, chers naufragés : notre ancien château, c'est cette grosse bosse de sable ! Le pauvre... Cette bosse ne se rappelle même plus qu'autrefois elle a été un magnifique château, avec mille tours et des donjons, et des dragons, et des gardiens et des soldats, car tout a été englouti par l'Océan Fantastique !

En plus, je crois qu'on est un peu au Pôle nord, main-

tenant, parce que gla gla ! Et quand il fait froid au bord de la mer, les naufragés changent d'habits juste après le naufrage. Ils font un feu et grillent un jambon pour le dîner sur la plage.

Nous, on pourrait manger un Petit Cochon en barbequeue, mais il a des habits qu'il ne peut pas enlever et on ne veut pas manger de la salopette en vinaigrette ! Et ça y est, il pleure ! Mais ne pleure pas, toi, « ouin ouin

ouin », c'est une blague, on ne va pas te manger puisque tu es un naufragé comme nous : donc tu as le droit de manger, mais tu n'as pas le droit d'être mangé ! Tu vois bien la différence, j'espère ! Donc courage !

Viens, Nounours, quelle chance, c'est les vacances !

Rentre vite dans le sac avec les autres et pas de rouspétance car on a gagné.

Et tout ça me chante un poème, d'ailleurs, que voici :

L'Océan Fantastique,
avec ses algues et ses vagues,
lave nos jouets en plastique !

C'est un poème d'anniversaire que tu peux apprendre, Nounours. Car tu dois devenir un Nounours qui connaît bien la poésie, comme tous les ours normaux.

La poésie, c'est bon pour les ours ! Pas seulement pour les hommes !

Table

Imprimé en France par *Partenaires-Livres*®
n° dépôt légal : 57914 - mai 2005
20.24.0788/8/04 ISBN : 2.01.200788.0
Loi n° 49-956 du 16 juillet 1949
sur les publications destinées à la jeunesse

"Here Is Your Soda"

That will be:
$54

$1 invested at a 10% average annual return will become $54 in 40 years.

Find out how to "Grab the Cash" and become a millionaire.

"WOW! Your Money"

The Retirement Thieves

Are They Locking Up Your Retirement?

Wally Wow will lock them up for you!

Find out how paying $50 per month on credit card payments can cost your retirement hundreds of thousands of dollars.

Oh Baby, Oh Baby!

40 cents a day will make your child a millionaire!

Invest just 40 cents a day from the day your child is born. By age 65, at a 10% average annual return, your child will have

$1,000,000.

WOW!

**Meet Wally Wow,
your own, personal
financial superhero.
He is your guide on
your journey to
financial success.**

Be Prepared to
be "WOWED!"

Wally Wow

Proudly Presents...

Built with The WOW! Numbers

Curt Rath
Ryan Rath

CR Publications

Published by CR Publications, 5901 Westcliffe Place, St. Cloud, MN 56303.

Printed in the United States.

Authors: Curt Rath, Ryan Rath
Co-Editor: Mike Reed, TDI Print Graphics
Creative Design: Heidi Nelson, TDI Print Graphics
Printing: TDI Print Graphics

LCCN 2007904978

ISBN 978-1-60402-075-5

Table of Contents

Fair Isaac and FICO® are trademarks and/or registered trademarks of Fair Isaac Corporation.

It's time to "live for the WOW!." Are you ready? Are you living a life that makes you say "WOW!?" Do people say "WOW!" when they talk about you? Make "WOW!" happen.

It's a game we all know. Wally just gives it his own unique twist. Put on your thinking caps and join him for your very own scavenger hunt.

It's really not hard to "WOW! Your Money." A few simple changes are all it takes. Follow a simple formula for success, and you will succeed. It's that simple.

We're just a couple of "average Joes." We're not accountants. We're not financial planners. And you don't have to be, either, in order to succeed.

Chapter 1
The Need for the Now

Most people suffer from the **"need for the now."** If you're like most people, the "need for the now" is why you need Wally Wow. The "need for the now" is Wally's way of describing why many people have financial problems. This book is Wally's solution to those problems.

If you're like most people, by the time you finish

*reading this book, the **"need for the now"***

*will change to **"live for the WOW!."***

"Live for the
WOW!."

If the "need for the now" were a short story, it would go something like this:

*When I was 25, I made pretty good money, but didn't give retirement much thought. It was so far down the road that it wasn't worth worrying about. At that point in my life, I said to myself, **"It's too early to worry about retirement. I'm only 25. I'll worry about that later."***

I started spending just about everything I made. I lived from paycheck to paycheck. Sometimes I thought about saving some money, but I never did actually save any. After the bills were paid, I spent my money on whatever I wanted at the time. Sometimes, I spent my money on whatever I wanted, before my bills were paid.

Before I knew it, another 25 years had gone by. I was now 50 years old. I had a huge new house, with a huge mortgage. I had two lease payments on two SUVs. I had two kids in two very expensive colleges. I had a small savings account and an equally small 401(k) retirement plan. At that point, I said to myself, "It's too late to start worrying about retirement now."

I kept on spending just about everything I made. I was 50 years old, still living from paycheck to paycheck. I figured it was too late to save, so I gave up on the idea. After all, it was all I could do simply to pay the bills. Sometimes I worried about retirement, but mostly I ignored it. After the bills were paid, there really wasn't much left to save, anyway.

Before I knew it, I was 67 years old. It was time to retire, but I couldn't. Social Security paid next to nothing, compared to my mortgage and other expenses. I'd been working for more than 40 years, but had little to show for it.

Just to pay the bills, I had to work two part-time jobs. During the week, I drove a delivery truck for less than $10 per hour. On weekends, I made $8 per hour greeting shoppers in a local department store. What I earned from these two jobs and my small Social Security check covered the mortgage on my big, empty, 17-year-old house, but not much else.

In the end, the "need for the now," left me in need.

Consider instead a different short story. This one is clearly different. Rather than being driven by the "need for the now," this one is based on "live for the WOW!."

*When I was 25, I made pretty good money, but didn't give retirement much thought. That was, until I read a book called "**WOW! Your Money**," **by Wally Wow**. After reading that book, I said to myself, "It's time to start thinking about retirement. I'm only 25. That means I have 40 more years to get ready."*

*I started saving whatever I could. I stopped living the "need for the now" and started living a "life for the WOW!." I kept Wally Wow's book close at hand. It was easy to read. It made sense. The guys who wrote it were clearly just "average Joes" like me, but what they wrote made sense. **And Wally Wow really was a superhero.** He made a real difference in my life.*

Before I knew it, another 25 years had gone by. I was now 50 years old. I had paid off my mortgage years ago, and always owned my fuel efficient cars. My kids went to good colleges, completely paid for simply by doing a few of the things Wally taught me in the "Wally Wow 30." My savings and 401(k) were large and growing. I said to myself, "I still have 17 years to save for retirement."

I kept on following Wally Wow's advice. It really wasn't that hard. In fact, almost everything Wally told me to do was simple. Things like not paying for soda from vending machines, buying fewer CDs and DVDs, eating more at home and less at restaurants … it was all simple to do. Sure, I ate out at restaurants from time-to-time. I didn't save all of my money. But following Wally Wow's advice made a huge difference.

Instead of "nowing" my money, I was "WOWING" my money.

Before I knew it, I was 67 years old. It was time to retire, and I was ready. My WOW! numbers had grown into some pretty big figures. I had few fixed expenses, and the ones I had were easily covered by my small Social Security check. Everything else was easily covered by the interest I earned on my WOW! numbers.

When my children asked me how I did it, I told them about Wally Wow. It was obvious his advice worked for me. So they started following his advice, as well. Like me, they stopped living in the "need for the now." Instead, they started living "for the WOW!." I was so happy for them. They were on their way, and I was naturally "WOWED" by their success.

Which story would you rather tell? In this book, Wally Wow shows us how to make the second story our own. Wally is our guide, mentor, and confidant. He is our own, personal financial superhero. He shows us the way to financial success.

Best of all, Wally Wow does it without complicated formulas. He makes sense. He guides us to riches we never dreamed possible, in ways that we never imagined. He shows us how to stop living in the "need for the now" and start succeeding in a "life for the WOW!."

Let Wally Show You...

☀ Why **you already have the money** it takes to accrue more wealth.

☀ How **you can have more money** for today while still saving for your retirement years of tomorrow.

☀ How you can **get the big payoff**, and add hundreds of thousands of dollars to your retirement accounts.

☀ How you can set up your 401(k) accounts to **easily average a 10% return** on your investments.

☀ Why **credit cards and other high interest debts** are retirement thieves.

☀ Why **inflation** is a **major threat** to your savings.

☀ How **you can beat inflation** and protect your savings.

☀ How to pay off your debts and fixed expenses before you retire, **so that you don't need to save as much for retirement.**

By following Wally's advice in these and other ways, you can:

⚜ Maximize your money's potential.

⚜ Become truly debt free.

⚜ Live with confidence, knowing that your savings will cover your retirement years.

⚜ Retire with confidence, thriving whether you have Social Security or not.

⚜ Live a more successful life, without sacrificing what's important in life.

In short, Wally shows you how to "WOW! Your Money."

He leads you on a grand adventure that starts right now. Are you ready? Wally hopes so. Because if you are ready, it's time to begin your very own personal journey to financial success.

Be prepared to be "WOWED!"

"This way
to the money."

Chapter 2
The Wally Wow 30

What is the Wally Wow 30?

What is the Wally Wow 30? It is many things. It's a list of money-making ideas. It's a starting point for bigger lists of money-making ideas. It's perhaps the strongest, most secure and most rewarding savings account you'll ever find. It's a set of high return, no risk investments. It's the power that drives how you "WOW! Your Money."

Why is this true? The reason is simple. In this chapter, Wally Wow gives you 30 proven money-making ideas. Each idea, on its own, can help you save thousands of dollars. Some only apply to some people. Some apply to all people. In any combination, they provide a road map for financial success.

Tap Water ▲ $2.00	Fancy Coffee ▼ $3.50	Online Music ▲ $1.00
Lottery Tickets ▼ $1.00	Programmable Thermostats ▲ $3.50	

"What are you investing in?"

Whether you follow this road map, or use it as a starting point for your own journey into financial success, one thing is certain. **The Wally Wow 30 can change your life.**

So let's get started. Wally is ready to go. Are you?

Wally Wow #1: Cool Refreshing Cash

If you drink bottled water, Wally's very first WOW! number may shock you. We're all supposed to drink about 80 ounces of water per day. That's five of those nicely labeled clear plastic, 16 oz. bottles. But if you just drink two bottles of water each day, at $1 each, you spend about two dollars per day on water.

Wally says, "Drink from the tap and save!" Here's what it looks like if you invest your $2 per day, instead of drinking it away.

Wally Wow #1:	Invest $2 per day [Approximately $60 per month]				
Rate of Return	5 Years	10 Years	20 Years	30 Years	40 Years
5%	$4,080	$9,317	$24,662	$49,936	$91,561
7%	$4,296	$10,385	$31,256	$73,198	$157,489
10%	$4,646	$12,291	$45,562	$135,629	$379,445

Wally Wow #2: Stop the Pop Madness

Like to buy soda from a machine at the office? If you bought your soda at the grocery store, you could save money. Say you spend $1.25 per bottle from the machine. You can buy the same amount at the store for $0.50. If you drink 1 bottle per day, you'll save $0.75 each time you bring your own soda to work.

Wally says, "Stop the pop madness!" Here's what it looks like if you invest $0.75 per day, buying soda at the grocery store instead of from a machine.

Wally Wow #2:	Invest $0.75 per day [Approximately $22.50 per month]				
Rate of Return	5 Years	10 Years	20 Years	30 Years	40 Years
5%	$1,530	$3,494	$9,248	$18,726	$34,335
7%	$1,611	$3,894	$11,721	$27,449	$59,058
10%	$1,742	$4,609	$17,086	$50,861	$142,292

Wally Wow #3: Hear the Money

Did you ever buy a music CD, just to get one song? Everybody has. But there's a better way. You can save lots of money using online music stores. If you buy a $15 CD, each song costs about the same as an online song. But, since you only wanted one song, you save about $14 buying the one song online, instead.

Wally says, "Hear the money." If you buy 5 songs per month, instead of 5 CDs, you'll save about $70. That's about $2.33 per day.

Wally Wow #3:	Invest $2.33 per day [Approximately $70 per month]				
Rate of Return	5 Years	10 Years	20 Years	30 Years	40 Years
5%	$4,760	$10,870	$28,772	$58,258	$106,821
7%	$5,012	$12,116	$36,465	$85,398	$183,737
10%	$5,421	$14,339	$53,156	$158,234	$442,686

Wally Wow #4: Let's Have Lunch

Lots of people go out to eat for lunch. While it may seem convenient to simply dash off to the nearest fast food place or snack bar, you can save a lot by bringing your own lunch. It's likely that you can bring your lunch for about $2 per day, versus spending $6 per day at the restaurant.

Wally says, "Brown bag it!" $4 per day savings lets you invest $20 per week, or about $2.85 per day.

Wally Wow #4:	Invest $2.85 per day [Approximately $85.50 per month]				
Rate of Return	5 Years	10 Years	20 Years	30 Years	40 Years
5%	$5,815	$13,277	$35,143	$71,158	$130,475
7%	$6,121	$14,799	$44,539	$104,308	$224,422
10%	$6,621	$17,514	$64,926	$193,272	$540,709

Wally Wow #5: DVD Savings

How many DVDs do you already own? Do you have a library of movies that you hardly ever watch? Why do you keep buying so many? If you only buy $100 worth (about 5 DVDs) instead of $500 worth (about 25 DVDs) you save $400. That equals about $1.10 per day.

Wally says, "Want to see a great ending?" Buy fewer DVDs and watch your savings soar.

Wally Wow #5:	Invest $1.10 per day [Approximately $33 per month]				
Rate of Return	5 Years	10 Years	20 Years	30 Years	40 Years
5%	$2,244	$5,124	$13,564	$27,465	$50,359
7%	$2,363	$5,712	$17,191	$40,259	$86,619
10%	$2,555	$6,760	$25,059	$74,596	$208,695

Wally Wow #6: Fuel Your Retirement

Driving around can be expensive. If gas costs $2.50 per gallon, and you drive 40 miles per day, in a car that gets 20 miles per gallon, you spend $5 per day on fuel. If you drove a car that averages 40 miles per gallon, you'd only spend $2.50 per day on gasoline.

Wally says, "Fuel your retirement." Invest $2.50 per day and you will get results like those shown, below.

Wally Wow #6:	Invest $2.50 per day [Approximately $75 per month]				
Rate of Return	5 Years	10 Years	20 Years	30 Years	40 Years
5%	$5,100	$11,646	$30,828	$62,419	$114,452
7%	$5,369	$12,981	$39,069	$91,498	$196,861
10%	$5,808	$15,363	$56,953	$169,537	$474,306

Wally Wow #7: $221,000 Movie Tickets

If you pay for premium digital cable service, just to get the movies, you really could be paying nearly a quarter of a million dollars to see reruns. That's right. If your premium package is $75 per month, you can probably get basic cable for about $40 per month.

Wally says, "Watch regular TV, or less TV period." Saving $35 per month is about the same as about $1.17 per day. Here's what that looks like.

Wally Wow #7:	Invest $1.17 per day [Approximately $35 per month]				
Rate of Return	5 Years	10 Years	20 Years	30 Years	40 Years
5%	$2,380	$5,435	$14,386	$29,129	$53,411
7%	$2,506	$6,058	$18,232	$42,699	$91,868
10%	$2,710	$7,170	$26,578	$79,117	$221,343

Wally Wow #8: Work Out and Save

Do you try to stay in shape? You know Wally does. Just look how great he looks in those tights! But staying in shape doesn't have to mean expensive gym memberships. If you pay $55 per month for a gym membership, you spend about $1.83 per day on working out.

Wally says, "Work out at home and save!" Here's what it looks like if you invest your $1.83 per day, simply by running down the street instead of on a treadmill.

Wally Wow #8:	Invest $1.83 per day [Approximately $55 per month]				
Rate of Return	5 Years	10 Years	20 Years	30 Years	40 Years
5%	$3,740	$8,541	$22,607	$45,774	$83,931
7%	$3,938	$9,520	$28,651	$67,098	$144,365
10%	$4,259	$11,266	$41,765	$124,327	$347,824

2

Wally Wow #9: High-Octane Cash

Gas prices are different, depending upon where you live. But no matter where you live, it's almost always true that premium gasoline costs more than regular. Since the average US car gets 22 mpg, and is driven about 13,000 miles per year, the possible savings really add up.

Wally says, "Go for a premium retirement instead!" Pay $3 per gallon instead of $3.30, and you average about $0.49 in savings per day.

Wally Wow #9:	Invest $0.49 per day [Approximately $14.70 per month]				
Rate of Return	5 Years	10 Years	20 Years	30 Years	40 Years
5%	$1,000	$2,283	$6,042	$12,234	$22,432
7%	$1,052	$2,544	$7,658	$17,934	$38,585
10%	$1,138	$3,011	$11,163	$33,229	$92,964

Wally Wow #10: The Electronic Savings Superhighway

While standard Internet service is slower, it saves a lot of money. Spending more time waiting for downloads can also free time for other things (like reading this book). If high-speed service costs $45 and dial up is $10, you save about $420 per year. That's about $1.17 per day.

Wally says, "It's worth the wait." You can use the time you spend waiting to enjoy getting rich on the savings.

Wally Wow #10:	Invest $1.17 per day [Approximately $35 per month]				
Rate of Return	5 Years	10 Years	20 Years	30 Years	40 Years
5%	$2,380	$5,435	$14,386	$29,129	$53,411
7%	$2,506	$6,058	$18,232	$42,699	$91,868
10%	$2,710	$7,170	$26,578	$79,117	$221,343

Wally Wow #11: Don't Play and Win

Yes, even Wally enjoys taking a chance on the lottery every now and then. But he doesn't throw money away gambling every day, or even every week. If a lottery ticket costs $1, and you buy one every weekday, you can save about $260 per year simply by not buying lottery tickets.

Wally says, "You always win when you don't lose." Saving $260 per year is like saving about $0.73 per day. Want a big payout? Invest the $0.73 per day.

Wally Wow #11:	Invest $0.73 per day [Approximately $22 per month]				
Rate of Return	5 Years	10 Years	20 Years	30 Years	40 Years
5%	$1,496	$3,416	$9,043	$18,310	$33,572
7%	$1,575	$3,808	$11,460	$26,839	$57,746
10%	$1,704	$4,507	$16,706	$49,731	$139,130

Wally Wow #12: Read All About It

Back in the old days, newspapers were sold by boys on the streets, crying out "Extra! Extra! Read all about it!" These days, you can get your news from a paper that costs money, or from many free sources such as TV, radio or online. With so many options, you don't have to go out to the streets to save.

Wally says, "Get your news free of charge." If a newspaper subscription is $150 per year, you save about $0.42 per day not paying for your news.

Wally Wow #12:	Invest $0.42 per day [Approximately $12.50 per month]				
Rate of Return	5 Years	10 Years	20 Years	30 Years	40 Years
5%	$850	$1,941	$5,138	$10,403	$19,075
7%	$895	$2,164	$6,512	$15,250	$32,810
10%	$968	$2,561	$9,492	$28,256	$79,051

Wally Wow #13: Now That's a Cover Story

If it works for newspapers, why not magazines? Most every subject is available online, for a fraction of the cost of magazine subscriptions. If you replace ten $30 magazine subscriptions with online options and other ways to get your news and information, you can save about $300 per year.

Wally says, "Forget the glossy photos. Go with the money!" Saving $300 per year is about $0.83 per day.

Wally Wow #13:	Invest $0.83 per day [Approximately $25 per month]				
Rate of Return	5 Years	10 Years	20 Years	30 Years	40 Years
5%	$1,700	$3,882	$10,276	$20,806	$38,151
7%	$1,790	$4,327	$13,023	$30,499	$65,620
10%	$1,936	$5,121	$18,984	$56,512	$158,102

Wally Wow #14: A Prescription for Wealth

Does your employer offer a Flex Spending account? This type of account uses pre-tax dollars to purchase things like prescription drugs, and many other items approved as health care expenses. You can save big money taking advantage of a plan such as this.

Wally says, "Healthy is good. Rich and healthy is better." If you can save even $50 per month, that's still $600 per year. That's about $1.67 per day.

Wally Wow #14:	Invest $1.67 per day [Approximately $50 per month]				
Rate of Return	5 Years	10 Years	20 Years	30 Years	40 Years
5%	$3,400	$7,764	$20,552	$41,613	$76,301
7%	$3,580	$8,654	$26,046	$60,999	$131,241
10%	$3,872	$10,242	$37,968	$113,024	$316,204

Wally Wow #15: The Style of Money

It's important to always look your best. Wally knows this is true. But, there are ways to look good and save. Consider haircuts. If you normally spend $25 on a haircut, but can find a different stylist for only $15, that is a $10 savings per month. You can save $120 per year on your 12 haircuts.

Wally says, "Looking good!" By saving $120 in a year, you save about $0.33 per day. That adds up to a stylish $63,241 over 40 years.

Wally Wow #15:	Invest $0.33 per day [Approximately $10 per month]				
Rate of Return	5 Years	10 Years	20 Years	30 Years	40 Years
5%	$680	$1,553	$4,110	$8,323	$15,260
7%	$716	$1,731	$5,209	$12,200	$26,248
10%	$774	$2,048	$7,594	$22,605	$63,241

Wally Wow #16: Insure Your Future

Do you plan on wrecking $190,000 worth of cars in your lifetime? That would be the equivalent of totaling about six $30,000 cars. Sure, it could happen. But we don't know anybody who ever did it. So, why pay the higher deductible on your car insurance? A $1,000 deductible versus a $250 deductible saves a lot!

Wally says, "Drive safe, and save big!" Ditch the $250 deductible that costs $200 per month for a $1,000 deductible that costs $170 per month.

Wally Wow #16:	Invest $1 per day [Approximately $30 per month]				
Rate of Return	5 Years	10 Years	20 Years	30 Years	40 Years
5%	$2,040	$4,658	$12,331	$24,968	$45,781
7%	$2,148	$5,193	$15,628	$36,599	$78,744
10%	$2,323	$6,145	$22,781	$67,815	$189,722

Wally Wow #17: Wedding Ring Riches

Years later, you'll understand that the size of your ring doesn't really matter. In fact, if you follow Wally's advice on this one, and retire with an extra $100,000 in your account, you'll look down at your beautiful ring and fall in love all over again.

Wally says, "It's about love, not diamonds." Buy a $1,500 wedding ring instead of a $3,500 ring. Add the $2,000 savings to your 401(k) and watch what happens.

Wally Wow #17:	Invest $2,000 one time				
Rate of Return	5 Years	10 Years	20 Years	30 Years	40 Years
5%	$2,567	$3,294	$5,425	$8,935	$14,717
7%	$2,835	$4,019	$8,077	$16,233	$32,623
10%	$3,291	$5,414	$14,656	$39,675	$107,401

Wally Wow #18: Wedding Day Wow

While we're on the subject of nuptials, we may as well dispose of the myth that big weddings add to marital bliss. They don't. What does add to marital bliss, however, is nearly $700,000 in your retirement account. Wally guarantees you'll like that number more than your faded wedding day memories at age 65.

Wally says, "It's just a party." So don't blow the chance to almost retire as a millionaire, just by doing this one simple thing. Throw a modest $7,500 wedding instead of a $20,000 one.

Wally Wow #18:	Invest $12,500 one time				
Rate of Return	5 Years	10 Years	20 Years	30 Years	40 Years
5%	$16,042	$20,588	$33,908	$55,847	$91,980
7%	$17,720	$25,121	$50,484	$101,456	$203,893
10%	$20,566	$33,838	$91,601	$247,967	$671,258

Wally Wow #19: Check This Out

It's the 21st century, yet some people are still paying their banks for the privilege of writing checks. How come? Listen, if your bank charges you a single penny to write a check, get a different bank. These days, there are totally free checking accounts all over the place. Get one and save.

Wally says, "Check it out." If your bank charges you $15 per month for a checking account, that's $180 per year, or about $0.50 per day.

Wally Wow #19:	Invest $0.50 per day [Approximately $15 per month]				
Rate of Return	5 Years	10 Years	20 Years	30 Years	40 Years
5%	$1,020	$2,329	$6,166	$12,484	$22,890
7%	$1,074	$2,596	$7,814	$18,300	$39,372
10%	$1,162	$3,073	$11,391	$33,907	$94,861

Wally Wow #20: Installment Savings

How much more car can you get for $50 per month? If your car payment is $300 per month, you pay $3,600 per year for your car. But if you can manage with a car that only costs $250 per month, you save $600 per year.

Wally says, "Steer clear of the status trap." You'll look just fine in your $250 per month car. Best of all, $600 per year adds up to a lot of retirement cash.

Wally Wow #20:	Invest $1.67 per day [Approximately $50 per month]				
Rate of Return	5 Years	10 Years	20 Years	30 Years	40 Years
5%	$3,400	$7,764	$20,552	$41,613	$76,301
7%	$3,580	$8,654	$26,046	$60,999	$131,241
10%	$3,872	$10,242	$37,968	$113,024	$316,204

Wally Wow #21: Deductive Reasoning

Every house offers savings opportunities. You can weather-strip doors and windows. You can turn down your thermostat in the winter, and turn it up in the summer. You can also seal your ducts. That's right. Sealed air ducts can save you big money, by keeping the expensive hot and cold air where it belongs.

Wally says, "Get a cost reduction." By taking the time to tape the seams on your ducts and vents, you can save up to $140 per year on heating and cooling costs.

Wally Wow #21:	Invest $0.39 per day [Approximately $11.67 per month]				
Rate of Return	5 Years	10 Years	20 Years	30 Years	40 Years
5%	$794	$1,812	$4,797	$9,712	$17,809
7%	$835	$2,020	$6,079	$14,237	$30,632
10%	$904	$2,391	$8,862	$26,380	$73,802

Wally Wow #22: Cold, Hard Cash is Hot

So, you've taped up your ducts and saved an extra $70,000 or so for retirement. Want to save even more? This energy efficiency thing is real. Get a programmable thermostat, that automatically adjusts the temperature in your home. It can save you another $100 per year, or about $0.28 per day.

Wally says, "Now that's cool, and hot!" By saving just $0.28 per day, your programmable thermostat can make you up to about $50,000 for retirement.

Wally Wow #22:	Invest $0.28 per day [Approximately $8.33 per month]				
Rate of Return	5 Years	10 Years	20 Years	30 Years	40 Years
5%	$566	$1,294	$3,424	$6,933	$12,712
7%	$596	$1,442	$4,339	$10,162	$21,865
10%	$645	$1,706	$6,326	$18,830	$52,680

Wally Wow #23: The Check's In the Mail

It's almost a given that you can pay many of your bills online these days. So, why keep buying all of those stamps? As of this writing, a stamp costs $0.39. If you mail 20 bills per month, you could be saving about $0.27 per day. Not enough to get your attention? How about the $50,000 it could become?

Wally says, "Catch up. Pay online." The electric company, gas company, banks, mortgage companies, and credit card companies all have secure online payment.

Wally Wow #23: Invest $0.27 per day [Approximately $8 per month]					
Rate of Return	5 Years	10 Years	20 Years	30 Years	40 Years
5%	$544	$1,242	$3,288	$6,658	$12,208
7%	$573	$1,385	$4,167	$9,760	$20,999
10%	$619	$1,639	$6,075	$18,084	$50,593

Wally Wow #24: Eat Better and Save More

This is a recipe for success if you're single. It works even better for couples and even better when you have kids. So what's the recipe? It's simple. Cook your own good food and eat at home. You don't have to do this all of the time, but if you do it most of the time, you will save grocery bags full of money.

Wally says, "Rich and tasty!" It's easy to save about $10 per meal by eating at home. Do this only six times per week, and you've saved $3,000 per year, or $8.33 per day.

Wally Wow #24: Invest $8.33 per day [Approximately $250 per month]					
Rate of Return	5 Years	10 Years	20 Years	30 Years	40 Years
5%	$17,002	$38,821	$102,758	$208,065	$381,505
7%	$17,898	$43,271	$130,232	$304,993	$656,203
10%	$19,359	$51,211	$189,842	$565,122	$1,581,020

Wally Wow #25: Snack Before You Go

When you go to the movies, do you buy the popcorn? Have you ever said to yourself, "WOW! That's a lot to pay for a snack." If you spend $15 per couple for popcorn and a couple of drinks, and go to the movies twice a month, you're spending about $1 per day on movie popcorn.

2

Wally says, "Eat before you go." Here's what it looks like if you invest $1 per day, by eating at home instead of buying movie popcorn.

Wally Wow #25:	Invest $1 per day [Approximately $30 per month]				
Rate of Return	5 Years	10 Years	20 Years	30 Years	40 Years
5%	$2,040	$4,658	$12,331	$24,968	$45,781
7%	$2,148	$5,193	$15,628	$36,599	$78,744
10%	$2,323	$6,145	$22,781	$67,815	$189,722

Wally Wow #26: Inflate Your Savings

This is definitely not a lot of hot air. When you drive on under-inflated tires, you lose money. Your car uses more energy (meaning more gas) when your tires are too low. So, keeping them properly inflated saves money. The amount you save depends on the car you drive, but on average you'll save about $110 per year.

Wally says, "Stay on the road to wealth." Under-inflated tires wear out more quickly, and waste fuel. $110 per year is about $0.30 per day.

Wally Wow #26:	Invest $0.30 per day [Approximately $9 per month]				
Rate of Return	5 Years	10 Years	20 Years	30 Years	40 Years
5%	$612	$1,398	$3,699	$7,490	$13,734
7%	$644	$1,558	$4,688	$10,980	$23,623
10%	$697	$1,844	$6,834	$20,344	$56,917

Wally Wow #27: Talk About Bean Counting

Are you grinding your savings away? Are you buying into the notion that you need fancy coffee that comes in a fancy bag with a fancy label? Do you know how much more that fancy coffee costs? A cup of it can be as much as $3. A cup of the good, old-fashioned coffee that comes in a can costs about $0.50.

Wally says, "Brew up the savings." If you drink 5 cups of coffee per week, you can save about $650 per year, which equals about $1.78 per day you can invest.

Wally Wow #27:	Invest $1.78 per day [Approximately $54 per month]				
Rate of Return	5 Years	10 Years	20 Years	30 Years	40 Years
5%	$3,672	$8,385	$22,196	$44,942	$82,405
7%	$3,866	$9,347	$28,130	$65,878	$141,740
10%	$4,182	$11,062	$41,006	$122,066	$341,500

Wally Wow #28: Anchovy Cha Ching

If you think eating fish on your pizza smells funny, imagine your shock when you realize that frozen pizza can help you save tens of thousands of dollars. That's right. If you eat just three $4 frozen pizzas per month, instead of getting $14 pizzas delivered, you will save $30 per month, or $360 per year.

Wally says, "Give me a pizza that action!" Invest the $1 per day that you save by eating frozen pizza, and you can afford all the extra cheese you want.

Wally Wow #28:	Invest $1 per day [Approximately $30 per month]				
Rate of Return	5 Years	10 Years	20 Years	30 Years	40 Years
5%	$2,040	$4,658	$12,331	$24,968	$45,781
7%	$2,148	$5,193	$15,628	$36,599	$78,744
10%	$2,323	$6,145	$22,781	$67,815	$189,722

Wally Wow #29: Call Wally and Save

When is the last time you actually read your cell phone statement line by line? If you do this, watch for minutes that you paid for but didn't use. If you see a trend, where you always have minutes left over each month, try a cheaper plan. If your current plan is $50 per month, and you switch to a $40 plan, you save about $10.

Wally says, "Make the right call." If you save only $10 per month, your investment is $0.33 per day. You can see how even this small amount grows, below.

Wally Wow #29:	Invest $0.33 per day [Approximately $10 per month]				
Rate of Return	5 Years	10 Years	20 Years	30 Years	40 Years
5%	$680	$1,553	$4,110	$8,323	$15,260
7%	$716	$1,731	$5,209	$12,200	$26,248
10%	$774	$2,048	$7,594	$22,605	$63,241

Wally Wow #30: Where There's Smoke

Now, let's be clear about this one. Wally doesn't like smoking. He doesn't go around putting out people's cigarettes. He does, however, tell smokers how much they're losing by continuing to smoke. A two-pack per day habit is at least a $4 per day expense, even with the cheapest cigarettes on the market.

Wally says, "Don't burn your savings." $4 per day is a lot of money. Invest it and it can add up to many hundreds of thousands of dollars.

Wally Wow #30:	Invest $4 per day [Approximately $120 per month]				
Rate of Return	5 Years	10 Years	20 Years	30 Years	40 Years
5%	$8,161	$18,634	$49,324	$99,871	$183,122
7%	$8,591	$20,770	$62,511	$146,397	$314,978
10%	$9,292	$24,581	$91,124	$271,259	$758,890

So, there you have it. **The Wally Wow 30.**

As you can see, even little numbers add up over time.

**It doesn't take long to find
$5, $10, $20, or even more each day
to be able to use to invest to become a**

millionaire.

You may have many more ideas to make you money.
Some of the ideas listed in the Wally Wow 30
may make you more or less money than the
price used. Just use the numbers relative
to your own personal situation.
You can also use these numbers as
examples to see how much different
amounts of money invested over different
periods of time can add up.

The point is to keep the idea and the concept in mind: that big
and small amounts really add up over time. And chances are you can
benefit from these or similar ideas.

So, do you see the power of the "Wally Wow 30?"

2

Well, believe it or not,
the Wally Wow 30
is only the beginning.
Wally has lots more to share.
In the pages and chapters
to come are many, many
more ways to save and win.
So, if you're ready, let's get going.

"Let's go!"

Chapter 3
The Fear of Money

Have you ever asked yourself, "What is my greatest fear?" Don't worry. It's not a trick question. Everybody asks that question at some point. It's natural.

When you ask the question, what do you say? Do you come up with crazy answers? Do you think of things like being trapped in an aquarium with a thousand snakes? How about being stuck in an elevator? Stranded on a desert island? What about the fear of your own money? Have you ever asked yourself about that one?

Fear of money? Has Wally gone off the deep end? Fear of money? No way. You probably never considered that fear of money might be your greatest fear.

Don't worry. You are not alone. Believe it or not, most people never admit their fear of money. Does that surprise you? It shouldn't. After all, what's so scary about money? It's just dollars and common sense, right? Or is it more?

You already know the answer to that one. Money is more than just a little scary. For many people, the fear of money freezes them in their tracks. It literally scares them stiff. Money, even our own money, can be one of the scariest things in our lives.

Consider the following situations. Do any of them sound familiar?

- **Have you ever avoided paying a bill, using the money for something rather than paying what you owe?**

- **Have you ever felt you might look stupid if you asked somebody a question about money?**

- **Did you ever pretend you had money that you didn't, in order to impress somebody?**

- **Have you ever been embarrassed by your salary, afraid to talk about how much you earn (or don't earn)?**

How about being honest with yourself, and others, about your retirement savings? One of the most common money fears involves retirement. People carry this fear their entire working lives. They are deathly afraid of retiring poor. Strangely enough, they are so paralyzed by their fear, that they never do anything about it.

Does this sound familiar to you? Have you ever felt that you are way behind the 8-ball? Are you afraid that you have far less in your nest egg than you need to retire at 67?

Wally says, "It is time to face our fear." Look it in the eye. Not knowing what to do with our money creates fear. The fear hinders positive action. It takes away our ability to produce positive results. Fear causes us to do nothing.

But as you've already seen, winning with the WOW! numbers takes action. We have to act, in order for the WOW! numbers to act on our behalf. We need to get over our fear, so we can do something.

So how do we get rid of the fear so we can take action?

The answer is knowledge.

❉ Knowledge gives us confidence.

❉ Confidence conquers fear.

❉ Eliminating fear gives us control over our money.

❉ Control over our money motivates action.

❉ Action makes the WOW! numbers work.

❉ When the WOW! numbers are working for us, we win.

So, let's look again at our fear of retiring poor. What knowledge can give us the confidence to get over this common fear?

No answer for that one? Well, don't get rattled just yet. You've already seen the Wally Wow 30. You already have 30 good ideas to help you conquer your fear. You are well on your way, with just those 30 ideas, to retiring a millionaire. And trust us: Wally still has plenty of tricks up his sleeve.

"Conquer your money fear and you will win with your WOW! numbers."

Fear of money is real. We all need to admit this. We need to learn more about money. That knowledge gives us confidence.

3

It eliminates our fear.

It gives us power over our money, leading to action and the power of the WOW! numbers.

Chapter 4
You Already Have the Money

Do you know why most people don't save enough for retirement? They don't think that they can afford to save. They pay the bills every month. They don't have any money left over. They assume this means that they can't afford to save. But they are wrong.

If you're not saving money, guess what? You're wrong, too.

The truth is that you and all those other people already have the money. You make enough right now. They make enough, too. No matter how much you make, you already have the money.

You already have what it takes to retire as a millionaire.

What do these 10 numbers have in common?

$4,800,400 $1,600,000 $900,000 $22,913,005

$48,000,000 $9,250,500 $5,000,000

$16,420,000 $14,596,075 $3,200,000

The answer: each represents potential earnings from a 45-year working career.

Now, we all know some people make more money than other people. Some people make less. That's just a fact of life. But did you know that a person who makes $10 per hour can retire as a millionaire? Do you believe it? It's true.

Why is this true? It is true because retiring as a millionaire only takes $51,300. **This is only $3.12 per day ($95 per month) for 45 years.** You can work for $10 per hour, starting at age 20, and easily save $51,300 ($3.12 per day). Invest it and earn a 10% average annual return. By the time you retire at age 65, your savings will grow to $1 million.

Here's how it works:

- $10 per hour x 40 hours per week = $400 per week
- $400 per week x 52 weeks per year = $20,800 per year
- $20,800 per year x 45 years = $936,000
- $936,000 - **$51,300** = $884,700

You can use $884,700 for everything else. Just save $51,300 ($3.12 per day for 45 years). Invest it and earn a 10% average annual return. You'll have right around $1,000,000 in the bank when you retire.

So why don't people save? Wally Wow thinks that the answer is they live for the now! Here are just a few examples of what he means.

- The couple with $3,200,000 wishes they had $5,800,000.
- The man with $5,800,000 wishes he had $9,250,000.
- The woman with $9,250,000 wishes she had more.

Do you think the man who earned $5,800,000 saved more for his retirement than the couple who made $3,200,000? It's likely that he did not. Because regardless of how much money these people made, they always wanted more. Yet the more they had, the more they spent.

The point is: making more money does not solve the problem. Most people who make more just spend it, anyway. Most people live too much for the now!

So how do we fix the problem? The answer might surprise you. **We don't need to make more.**

We just need to manage what we have more wisely. We need to take care of and make better use of the money we already have.

What does that mean? It means we have to think before we spend. But, we don't have to live poorly, in order to retire rich. **In fact, you can probably have a nice house, good car, fun vacations and still be able to retire a millionaire.**

Imagine you are 65 today. Ask yourself:

- Did you spend all your money along the way?
- Did you save for retirement?
- Did you keep your millions?

The whole point of imagining you are 65 is to think of these questions now. Think of them now, and answer them now. Answer them now, because when you really are 65, it will be too late.

Now is the time to start planning.
Right now, you have the money.
Wally is going to prove it to you.

4

"I've got proof!"

Chapter 5
The Life of a WOW! Number

Do you remember being measured? You know, the old "height and weight?" For some, it was once a year. For others, it was every time their Aunt Mary came to visit. "Oh, look! I can't believe how big you are!"

Of course, most of us stop growing eventually. We achieve a certain height, and a certain weight, and that's it. That's us. We're what we'll be, for the most part, for the rest of our lives.

The WOW! numbers are different. Unlike us, given time and compound interest, they never stop growing. In fact, the life of a WOW! number is all about continuous growth.

We stop growing.

The WOW! numbers never stop growing.

Maybe this is why it's so hard for us to understand them.

Whatever the reason, it's clear that most people don't understand the WOW! numbers. A recent banking industry survey showed how true this is.

The survey showed that less than half of us save $50,000 by the time we retire. More shocking is that 40% of us save less than $10,000. Did you read that right?

40% save less than $10,000?

Across a career, you can save far more than that by putting away less than a dollar a day.

To retire with less than $10,000 in savings is shocking, but true for many Americans.

The numbers don't lie. It's clear that most of us don't understand how WOW! numbers grow. We don't know what the life of a WOW! number is all about.

Fortunately, Wally does know. In the table, on the next page, you'll see Wally's insight into the lives of five **WOW! numbers:**

$20,000
$25,000
$30,000
$35,000
$40,000

5

In this case, the WOW! numbers are one-time investments. Perhaps they come from a year-end bonus. Maybe it was an inheritance, or profit from the sale of a home. In any case, look how the WOW! numbers grow over their lifetimes.

Results of Investing WOW! Numbers over a 35-year Time Period*

	$20,000	$25,000	$30,000	$35,000	$40,000
8%	$325,851	$407,314	$488,776	$570,239	$651,702
9%	$461,268	$576,585	$691,902	$807,218	$922,535
10%	$652,773	$815,966	$979,160	$1,142,353	$1,305,546
11%	$923,521	$1,154,401	$1,385,282	$1,616,162	$1,847,042
12%	$1,306,192	$1,632,740	$1,959,288	$2,285,836	$2,612,384

* based on interest compounded monthly.

Remember, these are one-time investments.
It's pretty amazing growth, isn't it? Imagine. You and your best friend each inherit $20,000. He uses his to buy a boat. **You invest yours. 35 years later, when his boat has long since sunk, you have between $325,000 and $1,300,000 in the bank. Now that's the life of a WOW! number.**

Of course, we don't all inherit $20,000 at age 30. We can't all count on the growth of a one-time investment. So what should the rest of us do? How can we work with the life of a WOW! number to succeed?

That's right. We should save whatever we can. Look at the next table, below. Do you see how just saving a single dollar or more each day can add up fast?

Invest this much each day for this long... You'll have	$1	$2	$3	$4	$5	$10
1 Year	$377	$754	$1,131	$1,508	$1,885	$3,770
5 Years	$2,323	$4,646	$6,969	$9,292	$11,616	$23,231
10 Years	$6,145	$12,291	$18,436	$24,581	$30,727	$61,453
20 Years	$22,781	$45,562	$68,343	$91,124	$113,905	$227,811
30 Years	$67,815	$135,629	$203,444	$271,259	$339,073	$678,146
40 Years	$189,722	$379,445	$569,167	$758,890	$948,612	$1,897,224

* based on 10% return, compounded monthly.

Do you see what Wally sees? Look at the column for just $5 per day.

5

If you save just $5 per day ($150 per month) over a 40-year time period, you end up with almost **$1,000,000.**

How does this work? Look at the table, on the next page.

Put away $5 per day (about $1,800 per year).

Year	Amount Saved	Amount Earned At 10% Interest	Year	Amount Saved	Amount Earned At 10% Interest
1	$1,800	$1,885	21	$37,800	$127,718
2	$3,600	$3,967	22	$39,600	$142,976
3	$5,400	$6,267	23	$41,400	$159,832
4	$7,200	$8,808	24	$43,200	$178,454
5	$9,000	$11,616	25	$45,000	$199,025
6	$10,800	$14,717	26	$46,800	$221,750
7	$12,600	$18,143	27	$48,600	$246,855
8	$14,400	$21,927	28	$50,400	$274,589
9	$16,200	$26,108	29	$52,200	$305,227
10	$18,000	$30,727	30	$54,000	**$339,073**
11	$19,800	$35,829	31	$55,800	**$376,463**
12	$21,600	$41,466	32	$57,600	**$417,769**
13	$23,400	$47,693	33	$59,400	**$463,400**
14	$25,200	$54,571	34	$61,200	**$513,808**
15	$27,000	$62,171	35	$63,000	**$569,496**
16	$28,800	$70,565	36	$64,800	**$631,014**
17	$30,600	$79,839	37	$66,600	**$698,974**
18	$32,400	$90,084	38	$68,400	**$774,051**
19	$34,200	$101,402	39	$70,200	**$856,989**
20	$36,000	$113,905	40	$72,000	**$948,612**

As you can see, saving just $5 per day (about $1,800 per year) produces almost a million dollars.

Pretty amazing, isn't it? The life of a WOW! number is remarkable.

Chapter 6
Making Your WOW! Numbers GROW

It's not complicated!

**WOW! Numbers just need
three things to grow:**

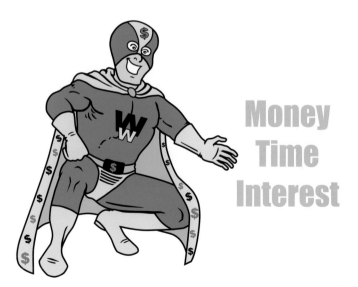

**Money
Time
Interest**

6

The truth is: money, time and interest are the keys to financial success. To see how this works, let's see what happens if we save **$150 per month.**

$150 x 12 months = $1,800

That's how much we save in one year. What if we save for 10 years?

$1,800 x 10 years = $18,000

Now that's not bad. But what if we add 10% compound interest? Now our WOW! numbers really start to grow.

Wally says…

"Time makes money!"

10 years = $31,000

Do you see the powerful combination of money, time and interest? After 10 years, we don't have just $18,000. With 10% compound interest, we have $31,000.

And what happens next is truly amazing.

We have $31,000 after 10 years. **Do we have $62,000 after 20 years?** No.

With the same 10% compound interest:

20 years = $114,000

Best of all, it keeps on working, just like that.

30 years = $339,000

It's the combined power of money, time and compound interest. It's how the WOW! numbers work. It's how the WOW! numbers work for you. Want even more WOW? Add another 10 years, and nearly triple your money.

40 years = $950,000

Still want more? Add just 5 years. Now your $5 per day grows to nearly one and a half million dollars.

45 years = $1,570,000

Think of it. At age 20, start saving about $5 per day. By the time you retire, you will have more than a million dollars for retirement. That's just $5 per day, to retire with over $1,500,000 **in the bank after just 45 years, at a 10% average annual return.**

Wally says...

"Make time and compound interest your two best friends and you will WOW! your money!"

6

Now, Wally knows that you may think that there's no way you can save $150 per month. Even if it only amounts to just $5 per day, it may seem like a lot. Well, don't worry. Remember, you're not alone. You have Wally. With his help, you can save $5 per day.

In fact, if your employer offers a 401(k) plan, you can probably already invest **$1.25.** Best of all, it is money that you didn't even know you had.

Here's how. Let's say you earn $5 at work. If you are in the 25% tax bracket, your pay check would be $3.75.

You earned $5, but only have $3.75 to spend.

Why not turn the situation around? Since your 401(k) uses pre-tax dollars, putting $5 into your 401(k) plan is very smart. Remember that without a 401(k), you only get $3.75 cash (spending money). But with a 401(k), now you get the whole $5.

"Can you believe it? Uncle Sam loans you $1.25 to earn compound interest over time."

Why is saving money so hard? Why don't we think of easy ways to save? Why don't we remember things like 401(k)s?

The truth is, our minds work in funny ways.

So fnnuy we cuold msiplel tihs etnrie book and you sitll wulod be albe to raed it, as lnog as the fsrit and lsat lteters are crrocet!!!

So if Uncle Sam will loan you $1.25 each day, all you need to come up with is an additional $3.75.

Does your employer match your 401(k) contributions?

If so, then all you need is $1.88 per day and you'll retire a millionaire.

Soon, Wally is going to show you how to get that $1.88, or even more.

6

┌───┐
│ **Wally Wow**   │
│   *Special Report*   │
└───┘

The Cost of Waiting is Expensive

"I was going to start investing at age 25, but then I thought, what is the big deal if I wait a few more years until I am 30?"

What's the big deal? How does $34,000 sound? That's the difference those 5 years would cost you, as outlined, below.

The table shows the cost to fund a 401(k)/IRA to have **$1,000,000 by age 65** (assumes a 10% average annual return).

Start investing at age	It will cost you	Cost per month	Amount you will have by age 65
25	$76,000	$158/mo.	$1,000,000
30	$110,000	$263/mo.	$1,000,000
35	$159,000	$442/mo.	$1,000,000
40	$226,000	$754/mo.	$1,000,000
45	$316,000	$1317/mo.	$1,000,000

It costs nearly $34,000 more by waiting just 5 years from age 25 to 30 **to have the same exact amount of $1,000,000.**

Wally Wow
Special Report

{PART 2}

It costs $83,000 more by waiting from age 25 to 35. This is $284 more each month. What could you do with $284 per month?

- Drive a $284 per month nicer car
- Buy 20 more DVDs every month
- Dine out 14 more times
- Buy about 90 gallons of gas
- Enhance your wardrobe with $284 worth of clothes and shoes every month

What happens if you wait to spend the $83,000 difference?

- Go on thirty $2,700 vacations
- Build your own theater with eight $10,000 high-definition big screen TVs
- Furnish your home with ten $8,300 furniture sets

You can have all of this because you start investing at age 25, instead of waiting until 35. $83,000 is a lot of money.

"Do you get the picture?"

6

Wally Timeout

Read this and you may proceed!

Oh Baby, Oh Baby!

Parents: 40 cents a day **will make your child a** millionaire!

What if you started putting money in an IRA for your children, right from the day they were born? How much would you need to invest, to help them have $1,000,000 when they retired? Would you believe $12.90 per month?

That is about **40 cents** a day. WOW!

That's right. Every month, you invest just $12.90 in your child's account. That's only about 40 cents a day. Think about it. Save just 40 cents per day, at an average annual return of 10%.

Your child can be a millionaire by age 65.

So, what has Wally shown you so far?

※ Compounding interest over time is what
allows your money to grow.

※ Only a few dollars a day builds a WOW! number
to fund your retirement.

※ Tax-deferred investing puts even more
money in your nest egg.

※ The longer you wait to start investing,
the more money it takes.

※ No matter what age you are, it is better
to start today than wait.

6

Wally Wow *Special Report*

The Power of Corn

Wally Wow says, "Compound interest is like corn." Sounds a little corny, doesn't it? But it's true. You see compound interest, like corn, produces big yields.

Think about it. Have you ever seen an ear of corn? How many kernels are on a single ear? It might surprise you, but a single ear has an average of about 800 kernels of corn. All that came from one original kernel? Now that's a WOW! number.

Now corn lives for one season, less than a year. But in its lifetime, it produces about 800 kernels for every kernel that's planted.

Now let's look at compound interest. Let's say you put one dollar in the bank, plant one "kernel of corn." Across your lifetime, your "season," how much corn will you produce from your $1? Well, if you live 70 years, **your single dollar will grow to about $1,000**, assuming a 10% return.

And what if you did what the farmer did? What if you planted thousands of kernels all at once? That's right. The answer would blow the top right off your popper!

7

Chapter 7
The Treasure is Already in You

Wouldn't treasure hunting be fun? Imagine yourself, decoding a secret map. You fight your way through hordes of villainous henchmen. Sail across stormy, wave-tossed seas. Endure blistering heat and sub-zero cold. Then, in a hidden cave high atop some far-off, volcanic island peak, you find it: mounds of ancient gold coins, diamonds, rubies, emeralds, sapphires … Now that would be exciting, wouldn't it?

Of course, for most of us, that kind of treasure hunt will never happen. We all love great adventure stories. We love heroes, damsels in distress, masked criminals lurking in the shadows. But we don't actually go off on treasure hunts, right?

Well, Wally has news for you. You are already on a treasure hunt. Right now, wherever you are, while reading this book. No matter how old, or young. No matter what you do for a living. Right now, you are on a magnificent treasure hunt. Find the treasure, and you can be rich beyond your wildest dreams.

"So Wally," you might ask. "Just where do I look?" After all, you don't have a map. You don't have mysterious clues written on parchment scrolls. You don't even have a sometimes-funny-but-mostly-irritating sidekick, for comic relief. So where do you look?

Would it surprise you to learn that the best place to look is inside yourself?

That's right. You have the treasure inside you. It's there right now. It's been there all along. You haven't recognized it, but don't worry. Wally is here to show you how to uncover the riches you already own. The treasure is already in you.

Are you ready to begin? Are you ready to go on Wally's $1,000,000 treasure hunt? The treasure is closer than you think. You don't have to search far. You don't have to search long. You just have to look.

"Wally's $1,000,000 treasure hunt"

Have you ever looked and looked and looked for something? Then, when you're about to give up, you see it. It's right there, sitting right in front of you. Isn't it strange how that can happen? It was practically staring at you the whole time.

The same is true when it comes to our money. We go out searching for ways to make money. We listen to just about anything that promises to make us rich. With all of these get-rich-quick ideas, everybody should be a millionaire by now, right?

Wrong! To become a millionaire, almost everybody needs a treasure map.

This chapter is your map. Follow it, and you will discover thousands of dollars of treasure. You will easily find $5 a day. It's quite likely that you'll find $10, $20 or more. And as you know, these are WOW! numbers. This chapter will give you the clues to find them.

Wally Wow
Special Report

7

Grab the Cash

**"Here's your soda, sir.
That will be $54."**

$54 for a soda? A bottle of soda?
Would you pay it? Who would?

Well, it happens every day. In fact, it
happens millions of times, every day.
People happily put $1 or more into
a soda machine. Every time they do this, they're not just raising
their blood sugar. They're losing a WOW! number.

It works like this. **$1, invested at 10%, will become $54 in
40 years.** That's right. **Without investing a penny more**, $1
will become $54. $10? 10 bottles of soda? They are worth
$540. What if you only buy a bottle of soda from that machine
twice a week? That's about 100 bottles per year. Guess what?
If you invested the $100, it would grow to $5,400.

So the next time you think about buying soda from a machine,
stop yourself. Imagine that you see $54 sitting in front of the
soda machine. There's a sign that says, **"I will pay you $54 to
not buy a soda."** What will you do? Will you still buy the soda?
Will you take the $54? Will you buy 20 oz. of carbonated,
artificially-flavored sugar water, or grab the cash?

Here is your first clue:

"Remember 54."

What does that mean? It's a clue, remember? Wally wants you to remember the number 54. Just remember 54. Remember just that single number. Got it? Okay, let's keep going.

What was that number again? Oh, yes. That's right. 54.

Why is 54 so special? Is it special? Is it just a crazy clue, one of hundreds, confusing and hard to follow? How can 54 be so special?

7

54 is special, because it's how much a WOW! number grows over 40 years. <u>Without any additional investment</u>, WOW! numbers grow to 54 times their present size. In 40 years, at 10% average annual interest:

$1	=	$54
$10	=	$540
$100	=	$5,400

And it goes on and on and on. Want to splurge on a $20 pair of sunglasses? That's right. Remember "54" and know that those cheap sunglasses are worth **$1,080** from your retirement fund. How about spending $40 on a cheap dinner and a movie? Yes, you got it. That's a cool **$2,160** from your treasure chest.

What if you don't have 40 years to invest? What if, like many people, you are reading this book later in life? Well, Wally has clues for you, too. In fact, he has a little game for you to play, called "Grab the Cash."

Take a look at the table, on the next page. For any period of time between 5 and 40 years, it gives you the "clues" you need to succeed. **Just line up the number of years you have until retirement, with the interest rate you think you will earn.** Do that.

Then you can "Grab the Cash!"

	INTEREST RATE				
Years	**12%**	**10%**	**8%**	**7%**	**5%**
40	119	54	24	16	7.5
35	65	33	16	12	6
30	36	20	11	8	4.5
25	20	12	7	6	3.5
20	11	7.5	5	4	3
15	6	4.5	3.5	3	2
10	3.3	2.7	2.2	2	1.5
5	1.8	1.6	1.5	1.4	1.3

Here's how "Grab the Cash" works. Let's say:

- You are 47 years old.
- You have 20 years before you plan to retire at age 67.
- The interest rate you think you will earn is 7%.

Use the table to figure out your "clue number," as shown, below.

	INTEREST RATE				
Years	**12%**	**10%**	**8%**	**7%**	**5%**
40	119	54	24	16	7.5
35	65	33	16	12	6
30	36	20	11	8	4.5
25	20	12	7	6	3.5
20	11	7.5	5	4	3
15	6	4.5	3.5	3	2
10	3.3	2.7	2.2	2	1.5
5	1.8	1.6	1.5	1.4	1.3

What does it mean? It means that every dollar you spend at age 47 is worth $4 in retirement. Spend $25 on a round of golf at age 47, and you lose $100 in your retirement fund. Grab the Cash!

7

Want to try another? Okay. Let's say:

- You are 32 years old.
- You have 35 years before retirement.
- The interest rate you think you will earn is 10%.

Again, use the table to figure out your "clue number."

	INTEREST RATE				
Years	12%	10%	8%	7%	5%
40	119	54	24	16	7.5
35	65	33	16	12	6
30	36	20	11	8	4.5
25	20	12	7	6	3.5
20	11	7.5	5	4	3
15	6	4.5	3.5	3	2
10	3.3	2.7	2.2	2	1.5
5	1.8	1.6	1.5	1.4	1.3

Your clue number, in this case, is 33. Now how much does a $25 round of golf really cost?

$25 x 33 = $825

Grab the $825 Cash!

This is no fantasy, folks. This is real. Every decision you make involves choices. So the next time you're ready to plunk down your hard earned money, play the "Grab the Cash" game. Ask yourself:

- **Do I really need that can of soda?**
- **Can I live without those shoes?**
- **Is there any earthly reason to buy a plastic frog?**

Or should I listen to Wally, and "Grab the Cash?"

Remember, even small numbers can be WOW! numbers. The money will allow you to retire someday. Do you really want to pay $54 for a can of soda? Of course you don't.

"Grab the Cash" is what good money managers subconsciously do all the time. It is how they get the money they need to retire. It may take you a little time, so use the table. The "Grab the Cash" game is how you can train your mind. You can learn the "clue numbers" by playing the game. It won't be long before your very own treasure appears, right before your eyes.

WOW!

Chapter 8
"Shift" Your Spending

8

Wally loves auto racing. It might just be his favorite sport. He loves the speed. He loves the power. Most of all, he loves the sound of shifting gears.

Do you know that sound? It is the sound of the engine winding higher and higher. Then there's a microsecond pause. Finally, the sound dips quickly then rises again as the driver accelerates. There's nothing like it in any other sport. The sound of shifting is a big reason why Wally loves racing, but it's not the only reason.

Wally also loves racing because shifting reminds him of the WOW! numbers. You see, in order to find WOW! numbers, people need to "shift" their spending. If you're looking for WOW! numbers, you most likely need to shift your spending, too.

Wally knows a lot about shifting his spending. Back in the day, before Wally discovered the WOW! numbers, he liked to eat at restaurants. Like most people, he never thought about how much those meals cost.

Then one day, he asked himself, "Why don't I have more money?" He had a good job. He had a nice, affordable house. But at the end of every month, it seemed like he was short. Something had to change. That's when Wally learned about shifting. He decided to shift spending away from eating at restaurants. The result was Wally's first WOW! number, and it was a big one.

To find his first WOW! number, Wally created his first budget. Shown below, it tracked everything he spent his money on. When he saw how much he spent eating out at restaurants, he could hardly believe it.

Wally says…

"WOW! I spent that much at restaurants?"

Spending Budget	
Revenue	
Salary	$3,000
Gift	
Other	
Total Cash per Month	*$3,000*
Fixed Expenses	
Mortgage/Rent	$1,000
Auto Loan	$250
Electricity/Natural Gas	$50
Gasoline	$100
Food (Groceries)	$150
Car Insurance	$150
Credit Cards	$200
Water/Sewer/Garbage	$50
Other	$50
Total Fixed Expenses	*$2,000*
Discretionary Income	**$1,000**
Flexible Expenses	
Restaurant	$250
Cell Phone	$50
Cable TV	$50
Clothing	$100
Furniture	$50
Magazine Subscriptions	$25
Entertainment	$150
Total Flexible Expenses	*$675*

By identifying and tracking this expense, Wally learned where he could save. The next month, he only spent $100 eating out at restaurants. He saved $150 in just one month.

Through a slight lifestyle change, Wally found a $150 WOW! number.

8

WOW!

Finding his first WOW! number was exciting. Wally realized right away that he was on to something. He knew the WOW! number was important; he just didn't know how important it was.

A short time later, Wally learned about compound interest. Right off the bat, he knew that he had found the place for his first $150 WOW! number. Wally shifted that $150 into his savings plan, where it has earned interest ever since.

You can easily do this too. What can you give up or scale back on? **If not restaurant food, is there something else?**

Wally says...

"I really did have the money."

Start tracking your expenses. As you track, your list of expenses will automatically be created. To help you, Wally suggests color-coding your budget, as follows.

Red = Fixed/Unavoidable Expenses

You can't get rid of these expenses, but you may be able to lower them.

Example: You need a phone, but maybe not caller I.D. or call waiting.

Yellow = Flexible Expenses

You have an opportunity to lower these significantly or eliminate them altogether.

Example: You don't need to eat out at restaurants anywhere near as much as you do.

Green = Shifted Expenses

Use the money you save in the Red and Yellow categories and "shift" it into a 401(k), pay extra on debts, or put the money into a savings/checking account.

Do this with Wally's old budget, and it's easy to see where he could shift his spending and find WOW! numbers.

8

Spending Budget		
Revenue		
Salary	$3,000	
Gift		
Other		
Total Cash per Month	*$3,000*	
Fixed Expenses		
Mortgage/Rent	$1,000	
Auto Loan	$250	
Electricity/Natural Gas	$50	
Gasoline	$100	
Food (Groceries)	$150	
Car Insurance	$150	
Credit Cards	$200	
Water/Sewer/Garbage	$50	
Other	$50	
Total Fixed Expenses	*$2,000*	
Discretionary Income	**$1,000**	
Flexible Expenses		
Restaurant	$250	Shift $150 to savings account
Cell Phone	$50	
Cable TV	$50	
Clothing	$100	
Furniture	$50	
Magazine Subscriptions	$25	
Entertainment	$150	
Total Flexible Expenses	*$675*	

Remember, this "found" money was not created from thin air. It was not given to you. You simply learned to make better use of the income you already have. You "shifted" money into your 401(k)/IRA, etc. Shifting your spending helps create more wealth either for today, or your retirement years of tomorrow.

Whatever your salary or wages, you have "X" amount of spending money each month. What you choose to do with it is your choice. If you find you are short each month, the shift your spending budget model will help you find the money that you need right now.

When Wally decided that something had to change, it was a big moment. When you decide it is time to shift your spending, it will also be a big moment. You will find, like Wally did so long ago, that shifting helps you:

- Identify exactly where your money is going.
- Utilize the wealth that you already have.

Once you identify where you spend your money, you will be able to pin-point all of the places where you can save.

Wally says…

"Shift your spending, and you will start finding your WOW! numbers."

The Result:
You get to keep the wealth that you already have.

Chapter 9
SALE Away With Wally Wow

Wally loves to sale. In fact, on any given shopping trip, you'll find him "saleing" right along. That's what he likes to call it "saleing." He doesn't have a boat. It's not "sailing" that he loves. It's the other kind. The kind that saves Wally money. The kind that's spelled "saleing."

You've probably seen Wally in the malls. He's always the guy having the most fun. That's because saleing is great fun. Best of all, saleing creates WOW! numbers in incredible ways.

9

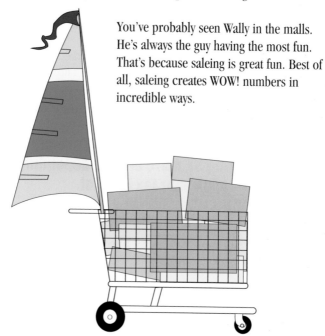

Think about it. Every time you buy something for less, you save money, right? Everybody knows that. It's no big deal. Or is it?

The truth is saleing is a HUGE deal.

Here's why. When you pay less for something, you get back more than you saved. Let us say that again. **When you pay less for something, you get back more than you saved.** Still confused? Well, that's why Wally is your new best friend. He is here to help. He can explain why saleing is such a big deal.

Let's say that you have $30 in your pocket. You see a pair of sandals that you like. The price tag says that they cost $30. But you have a $5 off coupon. When you pay for the sandals, you hand the cashier your coupon, and get $5 back in change. You just saved $5, right?

Yes, you did. But there's more. As Wally explained earlier, you only have money to spend that is left over, "after taxes." It works that way for all of us. When we get paid, our check is what Uncle Sam leaves behind. If you're in the 28% bracket, you have to earn $7, in order to take $5 home.

So, when you can save $5, it's really like earning $7, more or less, depending upon your tax bracket.

That's pretty great, isn't it? You save big money by paying less than full prices. It works every single time. When you spend less on the things you need, you actually make more than you saved.

Coupons are cash equivalents.

A good way to pay less than full price, again, is by using coupons. **Coupons** are also like stocks, but even better. They're better, because unlike investing in the stock market, with coupons you never lose money.

The returns are guaranteed.

Here's how it works. Let's say that you invest $10,000 in the stock market. You get a 10% return for the year. That makes you $1,000 richer, right?

You made $1,000, but you didn't make it overnight. Just dividing the $1,000 by 365 days, you see that you made $2.74 per day.

9

$2.74 per day is about $20 per week.

The same is true when it comes to using coupons and taking advantage of sales. Each time you use a coupon, or buy something on sale, you only make a little bit. But before you know it, over the course of a year, you've made good money.

Could you save $20 or more per week, by using coupons? Could you shop a little more, and save more, buying things when they are on sale? If you can, your coupons equal one nice return in the stock market.

Best of all, unlike with stocks, you don't need to invest $10,000 of your money. You need $0 upfront to get big money returns from **coupons.** After one year, you will make $1,000. If you invest the $1,000, and keep doing that over time, your **coupon savings** really grow.

$1,000 each year x 40 years
@ 10% compounding interest =
$500,000+.

So "hoist your main sale,
me hearties!" As you can see, above,
saleing is real money. It can create huge
WOW! numbers for your retirement.

Chapter 10
Drive Up Your MPG

Do you ever wonder why gas prices go up and down so quickly? Does it make any sense that you can pay $2.00 per gallon on Monday, and $2.50 on Tuesday? Have you ever wondered about this?

Wally wondered about it a few years ago. At the time, gas prices had just gone from $1.50 per gallon to about $3.00 per gallon. That was a 100% increase in gas prices. It happened almost overnight. Watching this happen, Wally realized a couple of things.

First, Wally realized that he was at the mercy of gas prices. After all, he couldn't just stop driving. He had to get to work, run errands, go shopping. Like most of us, driving was part of Wally's life. Whatever gas cost, he would have to pay.

10

Second, Wally realized that the car he was driving guzzled gas. Wally had a big SUV. It averaged about 15 miles per gallon. When gas was relatively cheap, he had never given this a second thought. But when gas suddenly went up to $3 per gallon ... Well, it made Wally think.

If you own a car, ask yourself, "Do I know what kind of mileage I get?" The answer to this question can help you discover another, very powerful WOW! number.

Buying a car that gets better gas mileage can save you money. **In fact, it can save you a large amount of money.**

To see how much, let's consider Wally's SUV.

- It averaged 15 miles per gallon.
- Gas was $3 per gallon.
- Wally was driving about 1,500 miles per month.

That meant that gas cost him $300 a month.

Now, let's say that Wally realized that $300 a month is a lot of money. In fact, Wally was so concerned that he traded in his SUV. He got a car that averaged 30 miles per gallon, instead.

- It averaged 30 miles per gallon.
- Gas was $3 per gallon.
- Wally was driving about 1,500 miles per month.

That meant that gas cost him $150 a month.

Just by owning a car that averaged 30 miles per gallon, instead of just 15 mpg, Wally saved $150 each month.

$150 per month is about $5 per day.

Remember when Wally showed you how $5 per day, over 40 years, grows to nearly $1 million? By driving a more fuel efficient car, you're almost there!

Buying a car that gets better gas mileage can be a huge hidden treasure for you. If you buy a car that gets 40, 50 or even 60 mpg you'll save an even greater amount.

What if gas prices go down? You still save. What if gas prices go much higher in the future? You'll save more. What will happen with gas prices is anyone's guess. But the simple truth is better mileage equals tremendous savings.

If you decrease your dependency on oil, volatile prices won't affect you as much. Buying a car that runs on an alternative fuel source, i.e. electric or is a "hybrid," i.e. gas/electric can be a huge hidden treasure in itself. It will instantly free up money that you previously were using for gasoline.

10

Stay Ahead of the Oil Curve

With gas prices as unstable as they are, it's a good idea to factor in some "what-if" scenarios when purchasing a car.

For example, when you buy your next car or truck, ask yourself some simple questions before you buy, including:

How much will the payment be?
How much will the gas cost me?

Let's say you buy a nice, big 4-wheel drive SUV. The answer to the first question, how much the payment will be, is $500 per month.

Now, what about the gas? If your new SUV gets 20 mpg (better than Wally's old truck) and you drive 2,000 miles per month, with gas that costs $2 per gallon, then you will pay $200 per month for gas.

2,000 miles / 20 miles per gallon = 100 gallons
100 gallons x $2 per gallon = $200 per month

Now, $200 per month may fit into your current budget. But as Wally found out not so long ago, gas prices can go way up, really fast. What if gas went from $2 per gallon, to $3 per gallon?

Wally Wow
Special Report

{PART 2}

At $3 per gallon, could you still afford to drive the SUV?
Remember, you're already paying $700 per month to drive it
($500 payment, plus $200 for the gas). If gas cost $1 more per
gallon, your SUV would suddenly cost you $800 per month.

**Could you afford to make an
extra $100 payment per month?**

If your answer is no, Wally has some good advice. Since gas has
already gone above $3 per gallon, plan for it to go there again. Do
the math. Buy a car that costs less per month. That way, if (when)
gas prices go up again, you will still be able to afford to drive.

There are other "oil" things you should think about. For example,
the value of SUVs and trucks greatly depreciates because of volatile
gas prices. When gas prices increase, their value depreciates even
more. This gives you less money when you sell your truck.

10

Also, when oil prices go up, it affects everything. Natural gas
prices go up (your heating bill is higher). Tire prices go up.
Airfares go up. Even perfumes and candle prices go up.
Basically, anything that is made from petroleum costs more
when oil prices rise.

Making wise decisions to decrease your dependency on oil will
keep you ahead of the curve. You will be better prepared when
oil prices unexpectedly rise (and they will). By staying ahead of
the "oil curve," your WOW! numbers will be safe.

Chapter 11
Max Out Your Credit Score and Win

Do you know your credit score? Wally knows his. Why? Because Wally knows, a good credit score saves him money. Knowing your credit score can save you money, too.

Your credit score, perhaps best known as your FICO® score, helps lenders decide whether or not to lend you money. For example, when you apply for a loan at a bank, the loan officer will look at your credit score. If he likes what he sees, chances are you will get the loan. Moreover, if your score is good enough, it can even lower the interest you will pay on the loan.

Unlike many things in life, your credit score is in your control. You can't control your boss. You can't control the stock market. You certainly can't control the weather. But your credit score is determined entirely by you. You are in complete control of whether this will be a high or low score.

"Some of your greatest hidden treasures lie within your credit score. Raising your credit score will free up potentially thousands of dollars you can use to fund your retirement nest egg."

Fair Isaac and FICO® are trademarks and/or registered trademarks of Fair Isaac Corporation.

A good credit score can help you save money. It can lower the interest you pay on loans. It can help you qualify for a bigger mortgage. It can even help you land a good job.

Your credit score is sometimes looked at by employers. It may be the deciding factor whether or not you are hired. Companies believe that if you can't be responsible with your own money, then they can't trust you with their money.

As you would expect, a bad credit score can hurt you in other ways, including:

- You may not get credit to buy a car, house, or even a cell phone.
- You may pay a higher interest rate on loans, services, or credit cards.
- Your insurance premiums may go up.

Your insurance premiums may go up? That's right. These days, some insurance companies look at your credit score. They place a lot of weight on it. In fact, many insurance companies offer a 10% to 25% discount based on a good credit score.

It's important for young people to know their credit scores, as well. Some colleges consider credit scores as part of their admissions process.

11

So what does all of this mean? In a nutshell, it means you need to know your credit score. You also need to do what you can to improve it.

Wally Wow
Special Report

FICO® Scores and How Much You Pay

A few points can make a big difference. In the table, to the right, Wally shows you how much you can save with a higher credit score.

In this example, pretend you want to buy a home and need a 30-year, $250,000 mortgage.

How much do you think you save by having a better credit score? $1,000? $10,000? $50,000? How about $100,000? The truth may surprise you.

To see the answer, assume that you have a credit score of 633. In the table, with a 633 credit score, you qualify for a 7.440% interest rate on your loan. With a 7.440% interest rate, you pay $1,738 per month. Over the life of the loan, you pay $375,600 in interest.

Wally Wow
Special Report

{PART 2}

Interest Paid on a $250,000 30-year Mortgage

FICO® Score	Interest Rate	Monthly Payment	Total Interest Paid
720-850	5.632 %	$1,440	$268,489
700-719	5.756%	$1,460	$275,559
675-699	6.293 %	$1,546	$306,665
620-674	7.440 %	$1,738	$375,600
560-619	8.253 %	$1,879	$426,330
500-559	9.408 %	$2,085	$500,735

But what happens if your credit score is higher? As you can see in the table, you can save a lot of money.

Do you see the savings? If your original score is 633, and you improve it to the 720-850 range, **you save $298 per month**.

That's $10 a day.

You save about **$107,000** over the course of the 30-year loan.

That's a WOW! number.

11

Now, mortgages are big loans, so of course the potential savings are huge, right? But what do you think the savings might be from other loans? For example, what if instead of buying a new home for $250,000, you just want to take out a $40,000 home equity loan? Take a look at how much a better credit score can save you in the table, below.

Interest Paid on a $40,000 15-year Home Equity Loan

FICO® Score	Interest Rate	Monthly Payment	Total Interest Paid
720-850	8.078 %	$384	$29,132
680-719	8.390 %	$391	$30,438
660-679	8.909 %	$404	$32,638
640-659	9.715 %	$423	$36,121
560-639	11.274 %	$462	$43,078
500-559	12.573 %	$495	$49,084

Do you see how much you save with a better credit score? What do you think happens with a car loan?

Interest Paid on a $30,000 5-year Car Loan

FICO® Score	Interest Rate	Monthly Payment	Total Interest Paid
720-850	6.084 %	$581	$4,869
690-719	6.876 %	$592	$5,537
660-689	8.875 %	$621	$7,256
625-659	11.247 %	$656	$9,358
590-624	14.348 %	$703	$12,208
500-589	14.853 %	$711	$12,683

Do you see how much you save? What if your spouse also needs a new car?

Interest Paid on a $20,000 5-year Car Loan

FICO® Score	Interest Rate	Monthly Payment	Total Interest Paid
720-850	6.084 %	$387	$3,246
690-719	6.876 %	$395	$3,691
660-689	8.875 %	$414	$4,837
625-659	11.247 %	$437	$6,239
590-624	14.348 %	$469	$8,139
500-589	14.853 %	$474	$8,455

11

Can you see the savings? How much do you think it all adds up to? Let's take a look.

Mortgage	
Improve your score to	720-850
You will save	$298 per month
Invest the savings at 10% return for 30 years	$673,625

Auto (1)	
Improve your score to	720-850
You will save	$75 per month
Invest the savings at 10% return for 30 years	$169,537

Auto (2)	
Improve your score to	720-850
You will save	$50 per month
Invest the savings at 10% return for 30 years	$113,024

Home Equity	
Improve your score to	720-850
You will save	$78 per month
Invest the savings at 10% return for 30 years	$176,318

If you add up all of the savings, your WOW! number is AWESOME! Simply by improving your credit score from 633 to 720, you save about $500 per month.

If you invest that over 30 years (the life of your mortgage) at 10% compounding interest,

you will have more than $1,100,000 in the bank.

More than $1,100,000? Wally is pretty sure he's got your attention now.

"So," you're probably asking, **"just how can I improve my credit score?"** It really isn't all that hard. It will take time, but you can do it. Simply pay attention to the areas that are measured, including:

❊ **Pay your credit accounts, and pay them on time.**
Late payments, non-payments and bankruptcies can hurt your credit score. Keep a solid track record of on-time payments and you can increase your score.

❊ **Don't max out your credit cards.** In fact, don't max out your available credit. If a credit card company sets a $5,000 limit on your account, staying well below that at all times can help to improve your credit score.

❊ **Don't apply for too much credit.** Lots of companies send you credit card applications. Don't apply. Keep the number of credit accounts you open to a minimum, just what you really need. Don't open accounts just because somebody says you are qualified.

❊ **Keep a good credit rating over time.** The credit companies look at the length of your credit history, as well as the history itself. A longer good credit history will help you improve your score.

11

❊ **Over time, work to have a mix of credit types on your credit report.** A good mix is to have just one or two credit cards (always paying early or at least on time), a car installment loan, and a mortgage. So long as you are paying the required amounts or more, early or on time, this type of mix will help to improve your score.

Are you interested in learning your credit score? If so, go to www.myfico.com. At this site you'll find out how to get your current credit score, as well as more information on how to improve it.

Chapter 12
The Key To Your Treasure

By now, having read many sections of this book, you know many ways to find your treasure. Wally has shown you that the treasure is already in you. You learned about the life of a WOW! number. You saw how shifting your spending can make you a millionaire. You know how to find your treasure. The question is, once you find your treasure chest, can you open it? Do you know where the key is that opens your treasure?

"Psst... Can you keep a secret?"

If you answered, "Yes Wally, I know the key to my treasure," then congratulations. Knowing where to find that key is very important. But if you're still wondering where to find your key, Wally has some good advice.

You see, just as your treasure is in you, the key to opening it up is you. That's right. You are the key. It is not a secret formula, or some exotic recipe for success. It is you. Go find a mirror. Look in it. Can you see the key? Well smile, because you are looking at it.

How much treasure you have when you retire is entirely up to you. The size of the treasure chest that you open in "x" years depends entirely on you. The amount of money you save is based upon the decisions you make. It is based on the attitude you carry with you every day. It's all about you.

Now, of course Wally is here to help. That's why he wrote this book. He wants you to succeed. He wants you to find your treasure. He wants you to open it. And all along the way, Wally is here to help.

Wally also hopes that you think of him from time to time. He likes giving you great advice. He loves knowing that you're doing well. He hopes that you remember him on the day when your treasure is opened.

Yes, Wally will always be here to help. He hopes that you think of him along the way. But in the end, he knows that the key to unlocking your financial potential is you.

You are the key to your treasure.

At the end of the day, when all is said and done, it's about what you want from life. What are the desires of your heart?

12

Your desires are what you pursue. They are what you think about. They are what you act upon. They are what you take action to accomplish. Every decision we make starts in our heart. Then we mull it over in our mind. Eventually, if the desire is strong enough, we may actually do something about it. The ones that we pursue are the ones we truly care about. They are our desires.

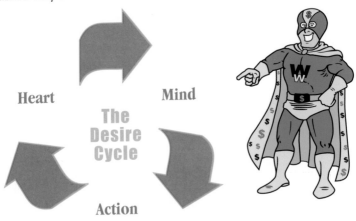

When thought transfers into action, results occur. Results are the aftermath of our decisions. Wally has shown you plenty of examples of possible results. Any one of the Wally Wow 30 has the potential to make you rich. How about going "saleing," or maxing out your credit score, or ...you get the point. When you finally take action, you are turning the key in the treasure chest lock.

Wally has shown you where to find your hidden treasure. But neither he, a financial planner, nor anyone else can open them for you. Only one person can. That one person is you. You are the key. You are the key to opening up and freeing the hidden treasures inside of you.

Have you found your key yet?

13

Chapter 13
Stash Your Cash

Have you ever thought about what it would be like to win the lottery? Lots of people dream about it. Very few ever win it. After all, if the lottery can afford to give away millions of dollars, it must be making millions and millions more. There's a reason why the odds of winning are "99,000,000,000 or something to 1."

For many people, winning the lottery would mean freedom from their jobs. Part of them wishes that they had the freedom to do whatever they want. They imagine a life without worry, without care. They envision walking up to their boss and saying, "I don't need this job anymore, thank you."

The idea is compelling. "I don't need this job," is what people imagine themselves saying. They love the idea. They picture themselves saying it. They picture their awestruck co-workers looking on in wonder as they walk out the door, for the last time.

Of course, reality soon sets in for most of us. Most of us are just plain, simple people. We are not millionaire professional athletes or billionaire software tycoons. We didn't grow up in mansions. We don't have chauffeurs, butlers and maids. There's no rich uncle to pay our way. Our lives are pretty much spent working. While the thought of goofing off all day is attractive, we know it won't happen. We need our jobs.

We'd still like to have some fun though, right? A little "goofing off" can be a good thing. But how do we do it in a positive way? How can we safely exercise our fun side? **Wally has an idea. It's called, "Stash Your Cash."**

The idea is simple. So far, Wally's ideas have been about saving money in interest bearing accounts. Now, Wally Wow simply wants you to save your money in a paper bag.

If you're shocked by this, take a deep breath. Inhale slowly through your nose. Exhale out your mouth. It is going to be okay. Before you stroke out asking why in the world Wally Wow lost it, relax. Before you run down the street shouting, "The king of compounding interest is gone," step back. Wally is definitely not crazy. He just wants you to have a little fun.

Of course, as you know by now, Wally always has a lesson in mind. This time, the lesson is simple. It's like one of those take home tests. It's "open book." It is so easy you don't even have to go to class and you pass.

13

Here's the idea. You are probably already finding WOW! numbers in many areas of your life. That's great. It means you've been paying attention. However, it's likely that some pretty big WOW! numbers are still slipping away from you every day. What Wally wants you to do is find them. And the fun part? It's called "Stash Your Cash."

While it may not be as fun as telling your boss "I quit," you do get to take charge. You also get to tell your money who's boss. You are. So Wally wants you to prove it, by taking your cash, and stashing it.

Here are the ground rules:

* Every time you find yourself about to spend cash on something unnecessary, stop.
That's the "you get to take charge" part.

* Rather than spend your cash,
figure out how much you were about to spend.

* Take just what you were going to spend out of your purse or wallet. Don't take any extra. Just the amount you were about to spend.

* Now say out loud, "It's time to stash my cash!"

* Grab those 1s, 5s and 10s. Shove 'em into your paper sack. "Get in there," you can tell them, as you stuff them into the bag.

Ways to "Stash Your Cash" include:

- You watch a movie at home instead of at the movie theatre. You save $20. Stash your cash!

- You eat at home instead of at the restaurant. You save $30. Stash your cash!

- You wash your car at home instead of at the car wash. You save $7. Stash your cash!

- You cut out coupons for a few things you need at the store. You save $5. Stash your cash!

Stash your cash from all your "Go Saleing" savings.

Stash your cash from the money you save from ideas in the Wally Wow 30, when you **"SHIFT"** your spending, or when you grab the cash.

Stash your cash on anything you were about to spend your money on, but DIDN'T!

13

Once your cash is out of your wallet and into your bag, go on with life. Smile knowing you just had a little fun. Then move on. But the next time you are about to spend more cash, take charge again. Stop yourself. Tell your cash who's boss.

Then stash your cash.

Try this for two or three months. By the time you empty out your paper bag, you will most likely be wowed. You won't believe how much cash you saved.

Now count it. How much is there? $500? $750? $1,000? Does it surprise you?

If you've never seen a bag of money before, get ready to be wowed.

Stash Your Cash and Dash to the Bank

Does it surprise you that many people quit their jobs because of pay issues? In almost any list of reasons why people quit, you're going to see pay rise right up to the top of the list. Some of the most common include:

- Management gave themselves bonuses and I didn't get a raise.
- So and so was paid more than me, and didn't deserve it.
- After all I did for them; they offered me a 10 cents per hour raise.

Wally's been there. He knows why people quit. He also knows that in many ways, the pay issues would never be issues, if people "stashed their cash."

Let's assume it is two or three months down the road. When you empty out your bag of "stashed cash," what do you have? Yes, of course, you have a pile of money. But what do you really have?

- You have extra money for your employer to match in your 401(k).
- You have more money to pay your credit card balances down.
- You have money to add to your savings plan.

Wally Wow
Special Report

{PART 2}

Most of all, you have options. You can afford an item you thought you didn't have the money for. You didn't get a raise, but it feels like you did.

You just found money that you had all along.

You just "stashed your cash."

"So go ahead. Stash Your Cash and dash, all the way to the bank!"

"Stashing your cash" isn't a long-term savings plan, of course. Wally wants you to take the bag to the bank once you see how much you saved. His goal isn't that you should save in paper bags. His goal is that you have some fun "stashing your cash," to physically see how much money you can save just by thinking about it, instead of spending it.

So go ahead. Take your cash and stash it away. You'll have some fun. When two or three months have passed, you'll be amazed how much you saved.

"WOW! Look at all this money. This is awesome!"

Chapter 14
Wally's Unassisted Triple Play

14

How much do you know about baseball? If you're like most Americans, you at least know the basics. If you're like Wally, you know a little more than that. In fact, after auto racing, baseball is Wally's second favorite sport. He loves the game: the managers' strategies, the drama between pitchers and batters, the storied rivalries, legendary players and passion of the game. Perhaps most of all, he likes the numbers.

Baseball is full of numbers, but none are more important than the number "3".

That's right. "Three" is the most important number in baseball. Think about it. A team gets three outs per inning. A batter gets three strikes per at bat. There are three outfielders. There are nine players on the field (three times three). Most really good batters hit about three hundred. The list goes on and on.

But perhaps the most amazing three of all is:

the triple play

Triple plays are extremely rare. Looking just at major league baseball, from 1876 to 2006 (130 years) there were less than 700 triple plays. In this century, it's estimated that the odds of seeing a triple play in a given inning are about 10,000 to one. That means, statistically speaking, you might see a triple play if you attended about 1,000 baseball games.

Only one team in the history of major league baseball has ever turned two triple plays in one game (that team just happens to be Wally's favorite team, the Minnesota Twins). But while the triple play itself is very rare, even rarer is the almost impossible unassisted triple play.

Across the same 130 years of major league history, there have only been 13 unassisted triple plays. Think about this for a minute. Out of all the hundreds of thousands of innings played, there have only been 13 unassisted triple plays. This incredible statistic makes the unassisted triple play one of the rarest feats in baseball.

Obviously, because it is so rare, there are very few players who have ever made this play. Only 13 have done it, and no player in the major leagues has ever done it twice.

"Batter Up!"

Wally Wow
Special Report

The Famous Thirteen

Here are the 13 major league players who have made
unassisted triple plays. In all of major league history, they are
the only players who accomplished this nearly impossible feat.

14

Neal Ball, July 19, 1909, Cleveland Indians (vs. Boston Red Sox)

Bill Wambsganss, October 10, 1920, Cleveland Indians (vs. Brooklyn)

George Burns, September 14, 1923, Boston Red Sox (vs. Cleveland)

Ernie Padgett, October 6, 1923, Boston Braves (vs. Philadelphia)

Glenn Wright, May 7, 1925, Pittsburgh Pirates (vs. St. Louis)

Jimmy Cooney, May 30, 1927, Chicago Cubs (vs. Pittsburgh)

Johnny Neun, May 31, 1927, Detroit Tigers (vs. Cleveland)

Ron Hansen, July 30, 1968, Washington Senators (vs. Cleveland)

Mickey Morandini, September 20, 1992, Philadelphia Phillies (vs. Pittsburgh)

John Valentin, July 8, 1994, Boston Red Sox (vs. Seattle)

Randy Velarde, May 29, 2000, Oakland Athletics (vs. New York)

Rafael Furcal, August 10, 2003, Atlanta Braves (vs. St. Louis)

Troy Tulowitzki, April 29, 2007, Colorado Rockies (vs. Atlanta)

Amazing, isn't it? Out of all of the many thousands of major
league players, through hundreds of thousands of innings
played, only these thirteen have ever made an unassisted triple
play. **In baseball, or in any sport, that's a WOW! number.**

So where is Wally going with all of this baseball talk? He's going straight to the bank, for you. That's right. Because here's the thing: while triple plays are rare, and unassisted triple plays far more rare, you (yes, you) can make your own unassisted triple play any day you want.

How can you do this, you may ask? It's easy. First remember the lessons Wally has taught you throughout this book. Now, pick just three of them. For example, you could pick:

- **Go Saleing**
- **Stash Your Cash**
- **Shift Your Spending**

You remember these three, right? If so, then you probably also remember how much each of these, on its own, can do to help you save for retirement. But what happens when you combine them? Can you imagine the possibilities?

Let's look at the numbers. Say you "go saleing" at the supermarket. You have a coupon for a delicious, herb-seasoned, slow roasted chicken. Normally that savory meal costs $10, but today it's half off with your coupon.

1. You just saved $5 by "saleing" your way through the checkout line.

Now, with a delicious chicken dinner waiting for you at home, you keep the cash you would have spent going out to eat.

2. If you were on your way to a $50 dinner, by eating your $5 chicken, you've saved $45. Stash your cash!

Now it's time to turn your very own, unassisted triple play.

3. By "shifting your spending" you take the $45 saved. Rather than spending it, you put it into your IRA or 401(k) account. Keep it there for 35 years at an average 10% compound interest and watch your WOW! number grow to more than $1,400.

14

By making your own unassisted triple play, you made yourself more than $1,400 in one night.

You had some great tasting chicken, only it was $1,400 less expensive! What a triple play!

See now why Wally loves baseball?

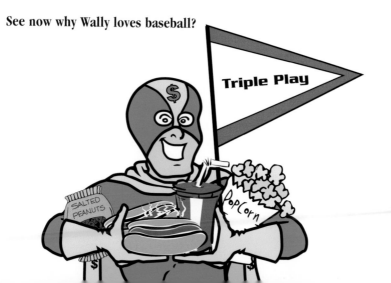

Buy What You Want - For Free

Clearly the focus of this book is how to save for retirement. The first step in doing this, as you know well by now, is to find your WOW! numbers. Wally has shown you many ways to do that. Then you save your WOW! numbers. Over time, they grow to enormous amounts, enough to fund your retirement in style.

There's more to the WOW! numbers, though, than simply putting them away for retirement. As you've seen, having enough for retirement isn't all that difficult. You just have to have discipline. You just have to follow Wally's advice in order to find your WOW! numbers. The actual amounts you need to put away are, as you've seen, relatively small. So what do you do with the rest of your money?

Well, obviously we all have bills to pay. We all need a place to live. We all need to buy food. We all have utilities. We have insurance. We have car payments. And yes, it's very true: the only two things in life that are certain are death and taxes. But as you've seen so far, making good choices leaves you with more than enough money to save for your golden years. So again, what do you do with the rest of your money?

Here's what Wally suggests. You can use your extra money, your very own extra hidden treasures, to essentially buy things that you want for free.

Wally Wow
Special Report

{PART 2}

Huh? Free? What? Has Wally gone off the deep end? Nothing is free. Or is it? Is there a way to get things for free, a way that really works? Wally thinks that there is.

14

Let's say you want to go to a concert. The ticket costs $75. You know how to "stash your cash," and really don't want to spend that much money. How can you afford to go to the concert? Can you think of a way to do it for free?

Now, if you said something like "sneak in through the back door to the stadium," Wally admires your inventiveness. He'll also enjoy reading about your arrest in the local newspapers.

But if you said, "Well, Wally, it's quite simple, really. All I have to do is use some of my hidden treasure," then Wally is impressed. You see, that's exactly how you can get things "for free."

Let's go back to that concert you want to go to. Can you save a little extra money by clipping coupons the next couple of weeks? Can you bring your lunch to work a few times more? Can you go out to eat one or two times less? You already know how this works. Remember "stash your cash?" Before you know it, by making just a few changes, over a short amount of time, you will have saved an extra $75. Now you can essentially go to the concert "for free." You didn't have to earn a nickel more. You're going to a $75 concert on money you already had.

Chapter 15
The Big Picture

What if you were paid your entire salary at the beginning of each year? What if you also had to pay for everything you bought at the start of each year?

If you were paid this way, would anything change? What about paying your bills? If you had to pay everything up front, would you spend money the same way?

For example, what about vending machine items? You know, like the ones in the break room at work. If you had to pay for all of your vending machine purchases ahead of time, would you do it? Would you willingly fork over $1,000 just for microwave sandwiches and soda? Wally doesn't think so.

Here's why. Buying a $1.25 vending machine soda and a $2.75 microwave sandwich and chips doesn't seem like much at the time. It keeps the break room in business, right? It is just $4. That's no big deal, right? However, if you eat lunch this way 250 times a year, your "vending machine lunch bill" would total $1,000.

"No big deal" purchases really add up.
A $4 per day lunch adds up to $1,000.

"Keep your money.
Don't stuff it in
the machine."

15

The $4 per day is what you see. It doesn't seem like much. That's because you think of the $4 compared to how much you make. If you make $400 per week, your brain tells you the $4 is just a tiny 1% of your earnings. Your brain tells you that you can surely afford to spend just 1% on lunch. Your brain tells you that the $4 price tag you see is so tiny, it's not worth worrying about.

That's the "little picture" that your brain creates, because of the way you are paid. You get a lump sum every week, or two weeks. The lump sum is typically several hundred dollars. In some cases, it's more. The problem comes when your brain compares the little things to the lump sum.

Instead of letting this happen, Wally recommends the "big picture" way of looking at expenses. He wants you to look at the big picture when making small purchases. One way of doing this, as outlined above, is to imagine having to pay for everything up front. It gives you the perspective of knowing that the little things really add up.

The next time you're about to drop money in the vending machine, remember the big picture. If that doesn't work, imagine handing the vending machine guy $1,000. Now, that's a "big picture" nobody wants to see.

Chapter 16
You Are the CEO

Can you imagine walking into work one day to find you'd been promoted without your knowing it? Yesterday you left as "Assistant Office Manager," and today you're the CEO? How would that feel? Do you think you'd be comfortable in your new role?

Very few people ever become CEOs. The air at the top of the corporate ladder is thin indeed. It takes a special person to run the whole show. Managing a few people and projects is one thing; being in charge of the entire organization is another. It takes a rare kind of person to be a CEO, don't you think?

Wally thinks it does. He thinks the kind of person it takes to be a CEO is so rare, in fact, that it's one-of-a-kind. "And just who," you ask, "is Wally referring to? Who is so great and rare that Wally Wow has dubbed him, "one-of-a-kind?" The answer may surprise you.

16

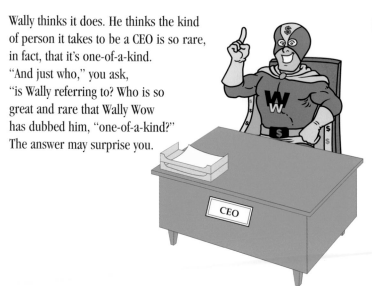

The answer may surprise you, because the answer is you. That's right. **You are the CEO (at least, when it comes to saving for retirement).** When it comes to developing a long-term strategy, managing assets, funding programs, developing business relationships, looking at the big picture … you are it. All of these things are what CEOs do. They're what you need to do, as well, in order to find your WOW! numbers.

It is up to you to find the money you need to retire. Only you can open up your hidden treasures in the Wally Wow 30. Only you can shift your spending, stash your cash, go saleing, max out your credit score and drive up your mpg.

> The fact is, your decisions
> make the difference.
> You determine how you
> will retire, or not retire.
> It is up to you.

So how are you going to do it, Mr. or Ms. CEO? Social Security probably won't help. In fact, the privatization of Social Security is becoming more and more of a reality each day. The government is asking you to make sure you have enough money to retire. They are asking you to be CEO. How in the world are you going to do the job? How will you make the right decisions to ensure your retirement?

One of the first things you can do is relax. Wally hasn't taken you this far, just to leave it all to you. Then, once you've relaxed, you can listen. Listen to what Wally tells you. Listen and learn.

Step 1: Think of Your Money as Your Company

"First," Wally says, "think of your money as if it were your company. Start managing your money as if it were your business." Now, for some people who already own their businesses, this is easy. They already think this way. And guess what? They are better at it than other people. But you don't have to actually own a business in order to act like a CEO.

Just start doing the things you've already learned in this book, to get money for your retirement. Find your WOW! numbers. Treat every one of them as if they were products or services, produced by your own company. Count on those products and services to drive revenue. Count on them to drive the profit you need in order to retire. Find your WOW! numbers. Invest them. Count on them.

Step 2: Remember You Already Have the Money

The next thing you can do is remember that you already have the money.

You can realistically create a multi-million dollar business for yourself by age 65.

The average couple makes **$2,000,000** to **$3,200,000** over their working career. What does this mean? It means you will almost certainly handle millions of dollars in your lifetime. That is a real chunk of change. It's not a bad size business for anyone to manage. You already have the money!

Step 3: Take Stock in Yourself

You can also take stock in yourself. Why trust others to handle your
money? Why put your faith in people you've never met? You know how
to find your WOW! numbers. You know what it takes. For example, take
a look at the diagram, below.

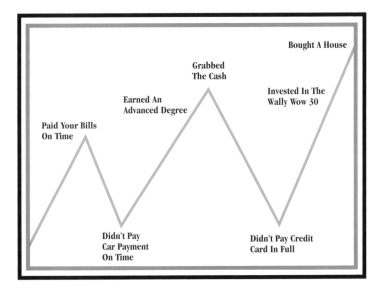

Do you see how the line graph works? It shows moments in life where
you put stock in yourself. Those are the places where the line goes up.
The graph also shows places where you don't put stock in yourself.
Those are the places where the line goes down. Picture yourself, sitting
behind your cherry wood or oak CEO desk. You have the line graph
displayed on your flat screen monitor. Will you take stock in yourself?

Step 4: Work for Yourself

The next thing you can do as CEO is to work for yourself. Wally knows that you have a big, important corporation to run. But it's also important to work for yourself. Spend a little time each week taking care of your money. It will make you hundreds of thousands of dollars over the course of your lifetime.

Ways to work for yourself include:

- Taking the time to find coupons.
- Looking for things on sale.
- Packing your own lunch.

By working for yourself, your WOW! numbers can grow very quickly. For example:

- Start at age 25.
- Work for yourself 1 hour each week.
- Save $17.50 per week ($2.50/day).
- You have almost $500,000 by age 65 assuming a 10% average annual return.

16

WOW! If you spent 10 minutes a day **packing your lunch and** saved $2.50 a day **as a result, you would have almost** a half million dollars**. WOW! If you spent a little time making your own coffee, instead of going to the fancy shop in the strip mall …**

How else can you devote just an hour each week to work for yourself?

How about paying yourself first? Do you think big time CEOs do this? You bet they do. That's why you read about how much they're getting paid all of the time. They make sure that they're paid handsomely when they take the job. They also make sure that they're paid handsomely when they're fired.

Look at it this way. You have the money each month to pay your utility bill, cable bill, phone bill, and all your other bills.

Do you have enough money left over to write yourself a check each month?

Wally says...

"Your check is in the mail!"

To put it a different way, if Wally sent you a bill for $150 each month, could you pay him? You would probably shift your spending, right? You would find a way to pay the new bill. You'd shift your spending just like you do for all the other companies that send you a bill. And if Wally invested this money for you, you would have a big WOW! number in your nest egg.

Well, Wally won't send you a bill each month. But pretend you have to pay a bill like this, and you will be paying yourself.

Step 5: Switch to Autopilot

One of the hottest trends in corporate America is outsourcing. It's hot now, and it's been hot for years. All the CEOs are doing it. You should do it, too.

One way to do this is to hire a "cyberbot" to pay your bills. Set up an automated system using the Internet or phone.

Your bills get taken care of and paid automatically.

This keeps you from making late payments that lower your FICO® score. It also ensures you get paid first, with money going directly into a retirement account.

As if that weren't enough, your cyberbot saves postage. If you remember from the Wally Wow 30, saving on stamps can make you $50,000 or more ($8/month invested for 40 years @ 10% interest = $50,000). $50,000 over 40 years would be $1,250 per year cash. It is like you gave yourself an annual $1,250 raise!

If someone came up to you and offered to pay your bills for free, AND give you $1,250 per year, **you would take it in a heartbeat, right?**

So what are you waiting for? Sign up today!

Wally says…

"Give me five! Up high. Down low. Too slow! Start this today, and never miss another high five or a payment!"

16

Step 6: Pay Yourself a Bonus

Wally is trying to decide whether or not to work for Company ABC or Company XYZ. He likes the people in both places. Both have interesting corporate cultures. Both offer similar challenges and opportunities. But there are some meaningful differences, including:

- Company ABC offers a 401(k) plan that will match $1 for every $1 he puts into his 401(k), up to 6% of his salary. In other words, for every $1 Wally puts into his 401(k), the company will put in another $1 on his behalf.

- Company XYZ does not offer a $1 for $1 match for his 401(k).

- Both companies are offering Wally a starting salary of $30,000.

Now, let's say Wally is 25 years old. He decides to be his own CEO. He decides to invest 6% of his salary into his 401(k). That equals $1,800 per year (just $5 a day!) He does this for only 5 years. **At a 10% average annual return $1,800 after 5 years will become $11,615.**

Now, Wally is 30. Without investing another dime, by age 65 that $11,615 will turn into $379,000 at a 10% average annual return. If Wally works for the company that matches his 401(k), he will have another $379,000 in his 401(k), for a total of $758,000.

Essentially, by choosing to work for Company ABC, CEO Wally Wow gave himself a $379,000 bonus. Not bad for a guy making $30,000 a year.

Step 7: Insure Your Assets

Another way to think like a CEO is to insure your assets. Choosing to work for a company that provides good health insurance benefits has a huge potential influence on your finances. As CEO, you can appreciate the positive difference.

Let's say that ABC Company's health insurance plan costs you $100 per month.

Company XYZ's plan will cost you $300 per month. The difference is $200 per month.

With the cost of health insurance factored into your total compensation, you really earn $200 per month more working at company ABC. The potential impact on your finances can be huge.

$200 per month invested at a 10% return for 35 years = $760,000. Essentially, ABC Company is giving you a potential $760,000 bonus. WOW!

16

Does your employer offer you a pension or something similar like a cash balance plan? This can also add up to hundreds of thousands of dollars more for you to enjoy during your retirement. The benefits plan your company offers at work is VERY important. It adds up. It can make or break your retirement plan. Good employers know this, and offer benefits to attract top talent. As CEO, you can have millions more in your nest egg by simply choosing an employer carefully.

Step 8: Spend Your Time Wisely

CEOs know the formulas for success. They know the numbers. One of their favorite things to say is, "If you can't measure it, you can't manage it." As CEO of your money, you need to know the numbers, too.

Consider the following formula: **Money = Time x Energy**

Now, Einstein's version goes a step further. But ask yourself, does this formula make sense?

In fact, it makes perfect sense. In every purchase, we relate what we buy with the time and energy we used to get the money. For example, let's say you make $36,000 per year after taxes (that is $3,000 per month). You want new furniture in your living room. You try to decide whether you want the furniture set for $3,000 or the one for $1,500.

When you do the math:
- It takes one month's salary to pay for the $3,000 couch.
- It takes one half a month's salary to pay for the $1,500 couch.

This means that to choose the expensive couch, you spend 160 hours of time and energy. If you buy the $1,500 couch, it only takes 80 hours of work to have that couch.

The question to ask yourself, as CEO of your money:
"How much of my life (time & energy) do I want to give up (spend) to have that couch? Is it 160 hours or 80 hours?"

If you base your decision on the answer to that question, you're thinking like a CEO.

Wally Wow *Special Report*

CEOs Buy Smarter

CEOs buy smarter. They drive their organizations to be efficient. They make sure that their managers do whatever it takes to drive out costs. This is your job as CEO, as well.

Let's say you buy the couch for $3,000. You pay with a credit card. The card has a 19% interest rate. Like most people you only make the 2% minimum payment due each month. Do you know what happens? Your $3,000 couch ends up costing you $13,000. You are now looking at close to 700 hours of your life to pay for a couch. Was it worth it?

Now that's a big question. Yet a bigger question is: How does this affect my retirement? It's not that you might have to work 80 or 160 hours to pay for that couch (although it is still a significant point). It is the fact that you could put the $1,500 towards your retirement fund if you bought the $1,500 couch instead of the $3,000 one. And, if you paid with a credit card, it would be a significantly larger amount that you could put into your retirement account.

If you are 30 years old, $1,500 would turn into nearly $60,000 by the time you were 67 at a 10% average annual return. Go for the $60,000! As CEO, how you spend your time is important. Equally important is paying with cash. **Buy smarter, so you don't have to work longer.**

16

Step 9: Moonlight

In corporate America, "moonlighting"
is discouraged. This really surprises Wally.
You see, while most companies have policies
about moonlighting, the fact is,
many CEOs do it themselves.

It's not at all uncommon for successful CEOs to get paid for their work
on outside companies' boards of directors. It's also common for them
to be paid as speakers, as consultants and in other ways. They can call it
anything they want, but Wally calls it moonlighting.

What if you moonlighted? What if you got a part-time job today that paid
$10 per hour? As CEO of your money, it's a good question to ask.

Consider the $10 you make moonlighting for just one hour. If you invest
it until age 65, you will have $537. For 1 hour of work at age 25, you
made $537 for your retirement at 65.

The way you could look at it is that you made $537 per hour at your job.

If you moonlight 10 hours each week, you would earn $5,200 in a year.
If you invested that $5,200 you would have $279,000 for your
retirement (again assuming a 10% average annual return).

Now look around today. Go to the supermarket. Go to the drug store. Go to the gas station. Do you see all of the "retirees" who are still working? Do you think that any of them are being paid $279,000 for working 10 hours per week?

As CEO of your money, you don't have to earn big bucks as a corporate director. Just work at the local supermarket or somewhere part-time now for 10 hours a week. As Wally showed you, that 10 hours a week at age 25 can turn into $279,000 waiting for you at age 65.

Can you work overtime at your current job and make $20 per hour? If you can, you should. At $20 per hour, the 10 hours spent moonlighting adds up to $1,074 per hour and $558,000 for your retirement.

What do you think about moonlighting now?

Wally Wow
Special Report

In Step 9 of this chapter, Wally showed you how moonlighting can really pay off. Work 10 extra hours per week at age 25, for $10 per hour, and you can invest $5,200. That money, at 10% interest, grows to $279,000 by the time you retire at age 65.

Now ask yourself, did you even have to work to make that money? By working a part-time job, you made $100 per week, or $5,200 per year. **Did you even have to work 10 hours to make $100 per week?**

What if you prepared two meals at home instead of going to a restaurant? What if you packed a lunch each day instead of going out? What if you made your own coffee instead of buying it at the coffee shop? What if you used coupons and saved $11 on your weekly grocery bill? **Does that add up to $100?** Let's see.

- Dinner at home twice: $15.00
  Dinner at restaurant twice: $50. **You made: $35.**

- Pack lunch 5 times: $15.00
  Eat lunch out 5 times: $50. **You made: $35.**

- Coffee at home 5 days: $1.00
  Coffee at shop 5 days: $20. **You made: $19.**

- Savings from coupons: $11.00 **You made: $11.**

Wally Wow
Special Report

{PART 2}

Do you see where Wally is going with this? He's telling you that you can make $537 per hour, without even working.

Do you make $537 per hour now? Maybe, but it's highly unlikely. Do you think you'll make $537 per hour working part-time in retirement? Of course you won't. So take charge, CEOs. You can do it.

16

Step 10: Sweat the Small Stuff

There was a time in corporate America when it was fashionable to say "don't sweat the small stuff." The theory was that it was unprofitable to spend any time on menial issues. The company was making too much money to worry about the little things.

Then global competition hit like a hammer driving in a nail. American companies were beset by foreign competitors. These foreign competitors enjoyed significant cost advantages. For American firms to compete, "sweating the small stuff" became not only fashionable, but also the norm.

As CEO of your money, you need to sweat the small stuff, too. Across your lifetime, you will make hundreds of thousands of decisions. Among all of those, only 10-20 are really "big." These include, of course, choosing a college, selecting a spouse, deciding on career direction, buying a house … But after those 10-20 big decisions are made, you still have at least 90,000 others to make.

In terms of your WOW! numbers, all of these other small decisions add up. Even if there is **just $1** riding on each of them, they add up fast.

So what do you do? What do the big time CEOs do?

Let Wally tackle the first question.

The key to successfully addressing big problems is to break them down into smaller issues. Don't try to solve it all at once.

Each of our lives begins with baby steps. Think of each day as one small little step. Consider each day a small step down the path to your financial dreams. For you, that might mean finding just one hidden treasure each week. For somebody else, it might mean stashing their cash just once a week at first. In any case, by breaking it down, over time such baby steps add up to big money for you.

Do you think CEOs do this? Of course they do. If nothing else, CEOs tend to be excellent problem solvers. **As CEO of your money, you can learn to solve problems step-by-step, as well.**

Let's say you are 40 years old. You want to retire at age 65. You might think to yourself, "There's no way I can save enough." Looking at it this way, you might be tempted to give up.

16

But what if you broke it down? One good way of getting started is to do the math.

- If you are 40, you have 25 years until you are 65.
- 25 years is 9,125 days.
- 9,125 days are 9,125 opportunities to impact your retirement nest egg.

As you can imagine, over 9,000 days of decisions will impact your finances at 65. And just think: you are not making just one financial decision a day. You are probably making at least 10 decisions every day, such as:

- Park in the ramp or on the street.
- Buy soda from the machine or bring it from home.
- Buy a newspaper or get free news from the radio, etc.

That's over 90,000 small decisions, or baby steps you will take on your way to the top. Do you see how breaking down the big problem helps?

90,000 little decisions become 90,000 potential WOW! numbers.

And as you know by now, 90,000 WOW! numbers can really add up.

Step 11: Keep Going, and Going, and ...

As you read the subhead, above, did you picture a little pink rabbit with a drum? If you did, you're part of Wally's generation. If you didn't, don't worry. The point Wally is about to make applies to you, as well.

By being the CEO of your money, you can create a multi-million dollar company. Someday, you can use your company to retire. To do so, as you've seen, requires an investment of time and money, combined with compounding interest. It also requires persistence. It requires you to keep going, and going and going.

With persistence, you create value. Just like CEOs create value for their companies, you can create value for your retirement. To do so, however, you have to pay attention to many things. You have to be persistent. Remember to:

- Work for yourself each week.
- Pay yourself first.
- Hire a Cyberbot.
- Consider working overtime or a part-time job.
- Work for a company that offers great benefits.
- Sweat the small stuff.

16

By doing these things, you will find WOW! numbers. You will be the CEO of your money.

Chapter 17
The Retirement Thieves

Have you ever been robbed? Wally hopes that your answer is "no." But if it's "yes," Wally hopes that the thief was caught. Wally hopes that the thief was punished. Thieves deserve to be caught and punished. The impact of their crime is far greater than the simple value of what they steal.

Would you invite thieves into your home? Would you open the door and say, "Welcome, boys. Come right in and take whatever you like?"

Of course you wouldn't. Nobody invites thieves into their home. You do everything you can to keep them out. If they do show up, you don't invite them in. You call the police.

In this chapter, Wally introduces you to one of the biggest thieves of all time. You may be surprised to learn who he is. You may already know him, and not think that he's much of a threat. But don't let him fool you. He's a much bigger threat than most people think. And if you let him into your life, he can rob you blind. "So what's his name," you ask? His name is **"Bad Debt."**

"Bad Debt" is "bad news." He's a low-down, dirty, cheating, snake-in-the-grass criminal that you don't want to deal with in any way.

In equal measures, bad debt always costs more than good savings returns. Put a different way, $100 of bad debt cannot be offset by $100 of good savings. The reason is simple. Lenders can legally charge you more interest on a debt than they have to pay you in interest on your deposits. Even with remarkable returns from a money market or other investment account, bad debt holds you back.

The key word in that last sentence is "bad." Some debt is truly bad, and some is actually good. There are differences between "good" debt and "bad" debt. If you borrow money to make more money, it can be good debt. However, if a debt does nothing but cost you money, it is clearly bad. Bad debt does not contribute to your financial well-being.

Examples of good debt:
Mortgage, auto loan, student loan

Examples of **bad** debt:
Credit cards not paid in full each month, or any other loans for unnecessary items

17

In today's world, credit cards often represent a form of bad debt. The fact is, they are too easy to get. They are too easy to use. In the world of e-commerce, credit cards allow us to purchase nearly anything, and have it delivered to our door. While this is convenient, it is also dangerous. The credit card makes it so easy to buy, people forget that they are spending real money.

Warning....Use at your own risk!

Credit cards are especially dangerous for young people. Today, companies target teenagers for credit cards. From Wally Wow's point of view, this is like tobacco companies targeting teenagers.

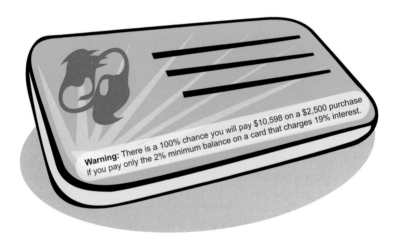

Warning: There is a 100% chance you will pay $10,598 on a $2,500 purchase if you pay only the 2% minimum balance on a card that charges 19% interest.

Bad debts and cigarettes: both seem harmless at first. You don't notice the harmful effects. However, soon you are addicted and don't even realize it. First it's one card. Then it's two cards. Before you know it, you have ten or more cards. Soon thereafter, your financial health is ruined. Like cigarettes, credit cards should come with warning labels.

The "No Payments, No Interest" Scam

Zero interest. No payments. No money down.*

We've all seen headlines like this by now. Did you notice the asterisk? Some folks call it the "little star." Whatever you call it, it typically points to fine print. Some folks call fine print "legal copy." Some folks call it "weasel wording." But whatever you call the thing that points to it, or "it," itself, typically "fine print" isn't very fine, at all.

After all, if the offer is so good, why does it have to be qualified by ant-sized type? Why is the fine print so small, anyway? What's it trying to hide?

In many cases, the trouble isn't what you find in the fine print. It's not what they tell you. **It's what they don't tell you.** For instance, in fine print you saw recently, they don't tell you:

> - If you don't pay off the loan exactly as specified, you will pay lots of interest.
>
> - The interest on such loans can be as high as a whopping 30%.

17

{PART 2}

How do they get away with it? Legally, they get away with it because they stay below criminal usury statutory limits. They point to how much good they do to stimulate the economy, offering very lenient terms. They also claim, somewhat accurately, that the market segments they inhabit are not well served. So, by offering credit to such people, they are in actuality doing a public service. Yeah for them. Not!

Remember, credit companies never think about how they can do you a favor. They are not in the conference room saying, "Gee, there are some really nice people out there. Let's give them a great deal. We don't want to charge as much as we know they will pay, because we're nice. We'll take it out of our own pockets, because that's how nice we are."

Here's the truth. The only reason companies start you with 0% is because they know most people will end up paying as much as 30% a year or two later.

Credit companies know this from decades of experience. They know how the human mind works. They know that people will take on more debt than they can rationally afford to pay off. **They know that right at the start, people didn't have the money they thought they had, in order to pay off the item.**

They know that they are targeting people who haven't read this book.

Wally Wow
Special Report

{PART 3}

Don't believe us? We've got the WOW! numbers to prove it. The following chart shows just how much and how long you will be paying for your credit card purchases if you don't pay them off right away and send in only the minimum required payment.

Total Cost / Time If You Pay Only The Minimum Payment Due

Card Balance	11% Total Cost	YRS	13% Total Cost	YRS	15% Total Cost	YRS	17% Total Cost	YRS	19% Total Cost	YRS
$1,000	$1,595	11	$1,815	12	$2,123	14	$2,590	17	$3,398	22
$1,500	$2,518	14	$2,906	16	$3,456	19	$4,305	23	$5,798	30
$2,000	$3,441	16	$3,997	19	$4,790	22	$6,019	27	$8,199	36
$2,500	$4,364	18	$5,088	21	$6,123	24	$7,733	30	$10,598	41
$3,000	$5,287	19	$6,178	22	$7,456	26	$9,448	33	$12,998	44
$4,000	$7,134	22	$8,360	25	$10,123	30	$12,877	37	$17,797	50
$5,000	$8,980	23	$10,542	27	$12,789	32	$16,305	40	$22,597	54
$7,500	$13,595	26	$15,996	31	$19,456	37	$24,877	46	$34,596	62
$10,000	$18,211	29	$21,451	33	$26,123	40	$33,449	50	$46,595	68
$15,000	$27,442	32	$32,359	37	$39,456	44	$50,593	56	$70,593	76
$20,000	$36,673	34	$43,268	39	$52,790	47	$67,737	60	$94,591	82
$30,000	$55,135	37	$65,085	43	$79,456	52	$102,024	66	$142,586	90
$40,000	$73,597	39	$86,902	46	$106,123	55	$136,312	70	$190,583	96

Based on minimum payments of 2% of balance with a $10 minimum payment.

17

Don't get caught in their trap.
Pay with cash.

So how can $2,500 of credit card debt end up costing you nearly $10,598? Look at the table, below.

Year	Balance Amount	Yearly Interest	Yearly Principal	Yearly Total
1	$2,377.82	$464.24	$122.18	$586.42
2	$2,261.60	$441.56	$116.20	$557.76
3	$2,151.07	$419.98	$110.53	$530.51
4	$2,045.94	$399.46	$105.14	$504.60
5	$1,945.95	$379.93	$99.99	$479.92
6	$1,850.84	$361.36	$95.10	$456.46
7	$1,760.38	$343.70	$90.46	$434.16
8	$1,674.35	$326.91	$86.01	$412.92
9	$1,592.51	$310.93	$81.83	$392.76
10	$1,514.68	$295.72	$77.83	$373.55
11	$1,440.65	$281.27	$74.03	$355.30
12	$1,370.24	$267.54	$70.40	$337.94
13	$1,303.28	$254.45	$66.98	$321.43
14	$1,239.58	$242.01	$63.70	$305.71
15	$1,179.00	$230.18	$60.58	$290.76
35	$405.07	$81.08	$38.92	$120.00
36	$358.08	$73.01	$46.99	$120.00
37	$301.35	$63.26	$56.74	$120.00
38	$232.84	$51.47	$68.53	$120.00
39	$150.12	$37.29	$82.71	$120.00
40	$50.24	$20.12	$99.88	$120.00
41	$0.00	$2.54	$50.23	$52.77
42	$0.00	$0.00	$0.00	$0.00

(Years 1–5 bracketed): $2,659.21

Based on minimum payments of 2% of balance with a $10 minimum payment at 19% APR

You can see that after 5 years of only paying the minimum payment due each month, you already forked over $2,659 for what you originally bought for $2,500. That is $159 more than the $2,500 purchase price.

You must be close to having that $2,500 paid off by now if you already paid that much, right? Wrong!

Look at the left hand column. Look at the 5-year mark for the amount still owed. **You still owe $1,945.** What in Wally's world is going on here?

What's going on is the powerful effect of interest. You saw how interest works for you, when you save. Now look at the amount of interest you pay, when you borrow. The interest amount is significantly higher. It takes a long time before you pay more towards the principal than the interest.

That is why it is so hard to pay the full balance of your credit card off when you make only the minimum payment each month. Almost all of your money is going towards interest.

17

In the chart on the previous page, Wally showed how paying minimums on credit card debt is a bad idea. In the example shown, a $2,500 credit card debt can cost you a total of $10,598. Paying the 2% minimum due, it will take 41 years to pay it off. This is because of a "domino effect" caused by the interest.

By only making a 2% minimum payment:

$2,500 @ 19% after **1 year = $2,964**
          after **5 years = $4,605**
          after **10 years = $6,244**
          and finally after **41 years** it will have cost you

$10,598

This is without putting another dime on your credit card.

In other words, when you make minimum payments, everything you put on your credit card ends up costing 2, 3, or even 4 times more than the price you originally paid.

Every $1 not used to pay debt, increases the debt as shown:

- $1 to $2 after 5 years
- $1 to $3 after 15 years
- $1 to $4 after 40 years

$10,000 credit card debt will cost over $40,000, if you just pay the 2% minimum due each month.

Regular Price

Your Price
With Credit
Card Debt

$1.25

$2.50 to
$5.00

17

As shown in the soda example, above, everything you buy on credit costs you more. The only way to buy on credit and not pay more is to pay off your card completely each month, on time, before it is due. In the soda example, if you paid only the minimum amount due each month, a $1.25 bottle of soda could cost you $5 by the time you pay off your bill.

Do you see how bad debt can suck the life out of your WOW! numbers? And it's not just for soda.

- A $10 meal costs you at least $20 if you don't pay this off in 5 years.
- That same meal costs you $40 if you are making minimum payments.
- A $50 shirt will cost you at least $100.
- A $3 gallon of gas will cost you at least $6.
- A $15 CD will cost you at least $30.

When you buy with credit cards and don't pay off the complete balance each month, even small fun purchases can add up to a large balance and become a burden over time.

- Pay only the minimum balance, and a $15 CD ends up costing you $60.
- A $3 gallon of gas costs $12.
- A $50 shirt costs you $200.
- A $2,500 TV costs you $10,000.

Can you afford $60 CDs, $12 per gallon gas, $200 shirts, or $10,000 TVs?

Wally Wow
Special Report

Credit Card Debt

About 80% of American households have at least one credit card.
At the end of 2002, the total credit card debt owed by Americans
was about $751 billion. Dividing that debt by the number of
households with credit cards produces an astonishing average
credit card debt of nearly $9,000 per household.

Does that number surprise you? Wally hopes it does. He hopes
you are part of the minority in America. He hopes you are
responsible with your credit. But if you do have credit card debt,
Wally hopes most of all that you pay attention in this chapter.

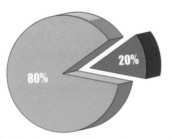

About 80% of American households have at least one credit card.

17

Unfortunately, America's average credit card debt has
skyrocketed since 1990. Increasing by nearly 200%, it has
become a huge center of controversy for policy makers at all
levels of government. Politicians from city hall to the White
House debate what needs to be done about the problem. They
should ask Wally what to do.

The burden of bad debt is why many Americans feel like they can't get ahead. Most of their money is going towards paying credit card interest.

The domino effect isn't over yet though. In fact, it has only just begun. This interest money you give to the "Retirement Thieves" could be going into your own nest egg.

Starting at age 20, if you keep a $2,500 card maxed out and keep paying only the minimum payment of $50 (over a 45 year period) and instead invested this money you would have over $500,000 by age 65 (at a 10% average annual return).

Do you realize what this means? Not only did you let "Bad Debt" into your home, **but you also handed him** $500,000. You lost $500,000 in your nest egg by giving "Bad Debt" $50 per month instead of investing in your 401(k). Additionally:

- You have lowered your credit score because your debt/equity ratio is higher.

- You will be approved for less of a mortgage.

That's right, add up the monthly payment of all your outstanding debts and this is exactly how much less mortgage payment you will be approved for each month.

Credit card debt not only **costs you money each month**, but also:

- Takes away from your ability to save for retirement.
- Lowers your credit score.
- Qualifies you for a lower mortgage.

That's a "quadruple whammy," courtesy of "Bad Debt" himself.

Ouch!

**Credit card debt goes far beyond what
our eyes can see. It surpasses what our
brains can fathom. It belies common sense.
Did you ever think that something that
seems so affordable could ever end
up costing you so much?**

If you're already way over your head in credit card debt, don't despair.
Remember, you have Wally Wow to help you. And help you he will, in
the very next chapter.

17

Chapter 18
Set Your Money Free

Wally got his first credit card during the fall of his freshman year in college. He remembers the day well. It was long before his transformation into a financial superhero. In fact, with a new credit card in hand, Wally was anything but financially savvy.

If you ever maxed out your credit card balance, you can identify with the young Wally Wow. If you ever made a late payment, you know what Wally was going through. Looking back on it now, Wally regrets many of his early credit habits. But some good did come out of those dark days.

Most of all, Wally's personal credit experiences helped him understand what folks go through. It's normal to feel alone when you're in debt; the world can seem pretty harsh when your bills grow larger than your paychecks. But in those times, you can count on Wally's support. He's been there. He got out of his mess. He can help you get out of yours. He can help you set your money free.

"Wally Wow to the rescue!"

Now, you may be saying, "It's too late for me. I already have credit card debt. I already made too many mistakes." Don't worry. Wally can still help. Remember, he's your own personal financial superhero. It's his job to rescue you!

Wally will help you. He'll help you even more if you start by helping yourself. A key to your success is to understand more about how you got into trouble in the first place.

Credit card debt is like a row of dominoes. The first one falls, hitting the second, into the third, on and on. First one part of your finances fails. Then more start falling down, one-by-one. It's like a long row of dominoes. Once they start falling, it's amazing how fast they can fall.

"Credit card debt takes you for a ride on a runaway "domino" train, derailing your financial and life-long dreams. Destination...**Bankrupt!**"

18

Every child knows how to stop a row of falling dominoes. You break the cycle. As adults, we need to apply the same logic to debt. Break the cycle, and we can all improve our finances.

The key to breaking the debt cycle is CASH.

Of course, if you're already in debt, where are you supposed to get cash? Wally knows it feels impossible. After all, if you had cash, you wouldn't be in debt, right?

It's normal to feel trapped. But with Wally on your side, there's hope. You already know many ways to generate extra cash. Apply the same advice Wally gave you about finding cash to save. It can also help you get the cash you need to get out of debt more quickly.

"More quickly" is very important. You see, it pays to pay down debt more quickly. Here's why. The longer you take to pay off a credit card balance, the more you pay. The more you pay, the longer it takes to get out of debt. It's a vicious cycle.

Ironically, many credit card companies encourage slow payments. **In fact, the credit card industry is just about the only industry where slow paying customers are put on the VIP list.** Think about it. The longer you wait to pay off your credit card, the more interest you pay. The credit card company loves this situation. It's where they make a ton of money. It's why they keep sending you more credit card offers, even when your credit score is already low because of current debt.

The following table shows you the powerful effects cash has on eliminating interest. The key point is this: **The more cash you use each month, the faster you get out of debt. The faster you get out of debt, the better.**

Dollars / Years Saved By Making Extra Payments Each Month

Card Balance	Extra Payment	Interest Rate									
		11%		13%		15%		17%		19%	
		Money Saved	Years	Money Saved	Years	Money Saved	Years	Money Saved	Years	Money Saved	Years
$2,500	$3	$349	4	$547	5	$881	7	$1,505	10	$2,871	16
	$25	$1,178	13	$1,725	15	$2,559	18	$3,937	24	$6,530	34
	$50	$1,431	15	$2,056	17	$2,983	21	$4,476	27	$7,211	37
	$100	$1,611	16	$2,282	19	$3,261	23	$4,813	28	$7,616	39

Do you remember what Wally told you in the last chapter? Do you remember how quickly interest can get out of control? In the example, Wally showed you how a credit card balance of $2,500, at 19% interest, ends up costing you $10,598. **This happens when you pay only the minimum amount due each month.**

But look at what happens when you use more cash each month, on top of paying just the minimum payment due each month.

• If you pay an extra $3 each month (10 cents each day); you will save **$2,871 and 16 years** worth of payments **GUARANTEED**.

• If you pay an extra $100 each month ($3.33 each day); you will save **$7,616 and 39 years** worth of payments **GUARANTEED**.

Can you find 10 cents per day, to save nearly $3,000? Can you find $3.33 per day, to save nearly $8,000? Of course you can!

18

WOW!

Do you see how this is a guaranteed return on your money? If you are paying 19% interest on your credit card debt, each $1 you pay towards that debt gives you a guaranteed 19% return. That is money you now have available to pay your debt down faster.

In fact, paying off credit card debt is usually the very best way to use your cash. It's even better than putting it into savings. This is because, as shown above, the return is much better. The money comes back to you, because you no longer are paying someone else the interest on that money.

When you pay off your credit card debt early, you are the recipient of the interest you would otherwise pay on your credit card.

Can you get a 19% **guaranteed** return on your money in the stock market? No. Can you get a 19% **guaranteed** return someplace else? If you can't, then the no-brainer decision is to pay off that credit debt.

"Guarantee yourself that 19% return. But remember, credit card debt is negative cash flow. Pay it off as soon as you can and turn that money into a positive cash flow."

The Exception to the Rule

Every rule has at least one exception. The rule about paying credit cards off early has an exception, as well.

*There is a common way to make more than you can by paying credit card debt early. That is your company's 401(k) plan **if your employer matches any part of your 401(k) contribution dollar for dollar**. Remember, it is a **100% guaranteed** return on your money. So in this case, the "no-brainer" decision is to invest in your 401(k). Get the guaranteed 100% return versus the 19% return.*

What do you do if you have more than one credit card balance to pay? The secret is to lower your interest rate. There are several ways to do this.

One obvious way to lower your interest rates is to simply ask for a lower rate. It doesn't hurt to call the credit card company. What do you have to lose? Simply call them and ask for a lower rate.

Sometimes, credit card companies can reduce rates while you're on the phone. Sometimes the answer will be "no." No matter what answer you get, it doesn't hurt to ask.

You can also lower your interest rate by consolidating your debt. Use balance transfers to move debt to the lowest interest rate you can get. Do you have a card at 13% interest? Can you move it to a card that has 11%? Consolidating debt to lower interest rates is a good idea.

18

After you consolidate your debt at the lowest possible interest, it's time to maximize your cash. Doing this is simple, as you will see. It is a proven way to get out of debt faster.

Here is how it's done. To maximize your cash, start with a list:

1. Create a simple list of all of your debts, including your house payment, utilities and of course all of your credit cards.
2. Mark each debt as either "must pay in full" or "must pay minimum."
3. Move all of the "must pay in full" debts to the top of the list.
4. Rank the "must pay minimum" debts by interest rate, highest to lowest.
5. Write down the monthly payment amount.

Here's an example of how your list might look.

Debt	Type	Balance	Rate	Payment
Rent	Must pay in full			$655.00
Electric	Must pay in full			$80.00
Water	Must pay in full			$20.00
Gas	Must pay in full			$40.00
Car Insurance	Must pay in full			$35.00
Telephone	Must pay in full			$40.00
Groceries	Must pay in full			$150.00
Car Payment	Must pay in full			$300.00
Credit Card 1	Must pay minimum	$2,500	19%	$50.00
Credit Card 2	Must pay minimum	$1,000	16%	$20.00
Credit Card 3	Must pay minimum	$5,000	13%	$100.00
Credit Card 4	Must pay minimum	$500	13%	$10.00
Credit Card 5	Must pay minimum	$1,000	10%	$20.00
		Total Bills		$1,520.00
		Take Home Pay		$1,700.00
		Left Over		$180.00

Now, in this example, you have $180 left over after all of the bills are paid. What should you do with this "left over?"

As you saw earlier, paying even a small amount extra each month saves a lot of money. If the balance on credit card #1, on the last page, is $2,500:

If you pay an extra $100 each month ($3.33 each day)**;
you will** save $7,616 **and** 462 months **worth of payments**
GUARANTEED.

By paying an extra $100 each month,
you will pay off credit card #1
462 months faster than if
you just pay the minimum.

So that is exactly what you do. Use your leftover balance each month, to pay more on the highest interest card. As shown in the example, you don't have to use all of your "left over" to make this work. But the more you use, the faster your debts will be paid. By sending an extra **$100** each month, credit card #1 is paid off **462 months** early. **To put it another way, it is paid off 39 YEARS sooner.**

So what do you do when credit card #1 is paid off? You guessed it. Apply your "left over" to pay off the next card faster. In our example, you now have another $50 extra to send to pay off the next credit card. This is how much you were sending to pay off credit card #1. Now that it is paid off, you can add that to your payment on the next card. Then you'll pay the next card off early.

18

Do you see how this works? First you take money from whatever you have left over after your bills are paid. You send it to the credit card with the highest interest rate. You pay that credit card off early. As soon as the first credit card is paid off, you move on to the second card. Pay it off early. Combine what you were paying on the first and second cards to pay off the third card early.

Each time you pay off a card, you have more to apply to the next card. Follow this simple method, and you will save thousands of dollars in interest payments. You will pay off your credit card debts faster, getting you out of the vicious cycle. You will also, of course, be able to start contributing again to your retirement savings.

The 50/50 Plan

If you're uncomfortable using most or all of your "extra" each month to pay down your debt, that's okay. We all have different comfort zones. You need to do what feels best for you. The key is to apply whatever extra amount you are comfortable paying to your highest interest rate debt. Even a small amount extra goes a long way.

The "50/50 Plan" is one way to do this. Use 50% of your extra to pay down debt, and 50% to put in your retirement plan. This way, you still make progress, and feel better about your money.

Wally Wow
Special Report

Bring In the Heavy Machinery

Wally says, "Bulldoze your debt
with lower interest rates."
To see what he means,
take a look at the table, below.

**Amount You Will Save By Consolidating a $2,500
Credit Card Balance Charging a 19% Interest Rate**

Consolidated Rate	Money Saved	Years Saved
11%	$6,234	23
13%	$5,510	20
15%	$4,475	17
17%	$2,865	11
19%	$0	0

18

*Based on minimum payments of 2% of balance
with a $10 minimum payment.*

Wally Wow
Special Report

{PART 2}

Just look at the difference between a 19% and an 11% interest
rate on $2,500 of credit card debt. If you can consolidate your
credit card debt to a lower interest rate, do it. If you are only
paying the minimum amount due each month, **this move alone
will save you $6,234 and 23 years worth of payments.**

If consolidating your debt is
"bulldozing," then paying it
off from the highest to lowest
interest rate is **"steamrolling."**

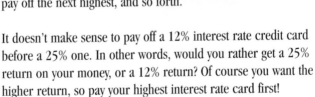

As shown in this chapter,
first you pay more on the
highest interest rate
card. Then pay off
your next highest
interest debt. Then
pay off the next highest, and so forth.

It doesn't make sense to pay off a 12% interest rate credit card
before a 25% one. In other words, would you rather get a 25%
return on your money, or a 12% return? Of course you want the
higher return, so pay your highest interest rate card first!

The combination of debt consolidation (bulldozing) and paying
off your highest interest rate debt first (steamrolling) is
definitely a "heavy equipment" advantage.

Obviously, paying down your debts requires discipline. There are times when you have to make tough choices.

For example, say your debt payment plan requires that you apply $100 each month to your highest interest credit card. You go for a couple of months. Things are going well. Then one day a friend asks you to go to a concert. The ticket is $100. What do you do?

This is where discipline comes in. Perhaps, at the moment of truth, it helps to stay focused on the facts:

- $2,500 owed on a credit card
- 19% interest
- 2% minimum payments per month
- Total payments more than $10,000

If you can spend **$2,500 less** over the next year and use that money to instead pay off your credit card balance, you would **save over $7,500 and 40 years of payments** on that $2,500 debt.

If you wrote the check to pay the full balance of $2,500 you would save the $7,500+ you would spend in interest. Hence, you would be $7,500 richer.

18

To put it another way:

For every $1 you use to pay your credit card off early, you save or make a little over $3.

So, now your friend asks you to pay $100 for a concert ticket. You want to go. You have the $100.

But if you use that $100 to pay your credit card, you will save $300. You actually will make $300 by not going to the concert.

So what do you do? Wally suggests telling your friend to enjoy the show. In a few months, when your debts are paid, you can stash more than enough cash to enjoy concerts whenever you want to go.

This doesn't just work for concert tickets, of course. Say that you want a $50 shirt. If you use the money to pay down your credit card, your $50 is really worth $150. And unlike when you stash your cash to invest, you don't have to wait 20, 30 or 40 years to collect. If you are paying 19% interest on a credit card and you pay it down, it is a **guaranteed** return. Why risk getting a 10% return in the stock market when you can guarantee yourself a 19% return and some big cash now?

Wally Wow
Set Your Money Free
Checklist

Use these steps to pay down your credit
card debt to SET YOUR MONEY FREE.

❉ Pay your highest interest rate loans or accounts
that are currently overdue first.

❉ Set up your Cyberbot to make your payments automatically
each month and never miss a payment.

❉ Always make the minimum payment so your FICO® score
doesn't go down and make things worse.

❉ After that send in any extra money you can, paying off
the highest interest rate debt first.

❉ If you have a high FICO score, get an introductory 0%
credit card that allows you to transfer your balances.

❉ Consolidate your loans if you can get a better interest rate.

❉ Use "The Wally Wow 30," "Go Saleing," "Stash Your Cash,"
"Shift Your Spending," etc. and get the cash you need.

❉ Send in all the extra cash you possibly can until your
balance reaches $0. **Set your money free!**

18

Paying down your debt also improves your credit score. When you improve your credit score you get better interest rates when you need a loan. As you pay down even more of your credit card balances, your debt/credit ratio will continue to decrease. Your credit score will keep improving.

For example, say you have a balance of $2,500. If your credit limit is $5,000, you have a debt to credit ratio of .5. If you pay $500 off of your card, you will have a balance of $2,000, which will lower your debt to credit ratio to .4. This improves your credit score.

By paying off your debt,
you reverse the negative
domino effect, and instead
create a positive domino effect
for you and your money.
You beat the Retirement Thieves!

Best of all, you free up your money,
and every dollar you set free
is a WOW! number.

Chapter 19
Your Own Personal Gold Mind

No, it's not a typo. Wally spelled it correctly. He means it, exactly the way he spelled it. Your own personal gold mind is Wally's way of saying, "Your mind is a valuable thing." To put it another way, your mind is gold.

Wally is right. Your mind is worth millions, if you use it properly. It can be worth billions, if you combine proper use with a little luck. In any case, the information in your brain is more than valuable. It is invaluable. If you develop your knowledge, so that others can benefit from it, you can make lots of money. Even more importantly, you can help make the world a better place for all of us.

You can buy knowledge in a book. You can download knowledge from millions of websites. You can use search engines to focus your search on any one of billions of subjects. But no matter where you get knowledge, **the key is to use it**. A positive by-product of using knowledge is to profit by it. You have to apply what you learned. Simply telling your employer that you read a book most likely will not get you a raise; however, using what you learn to make valuable contributions can get you a raise, and much more.

So ask yourself: what information do I have that can be valuable to others? You may already know the answer to that question. You may in fact already be profiting by what you know. But if you're like many people, you may still be searching not only for the knowledge you need, but also for the way you will get it. The question you must answer is: **How valuable can your gold mind become?**

Staying in school really does pay

No diploma	*= average of $18,734 per year*
High school diploma	*= average of $27,915 per year*
Bachelor's degree	*= average of $51,206 per year*
Advanced degree	*= average of $74,602 per year*

Source: The U.S. Census Bureau 2004

To start your search, consider for a minute how much your gold mind can be worth. **Let's take a look at the potential WOW! numbers your gold mind can make you.** These are the average lifetime earnings of an individual with:

No diploma	$ 940,000
High school diploma	$1,310,000
Bachelor's degree	$2,200,000
Advanced degree	$2,980,000

As you can see, high school graduates earn about $400,000 more than non-grads. College grads earn on average about $900,000 more than high school grads. The lesson: If you didn't finish high school, get your GED. If you don't already have a bachelor's degree, you should get one.

"But Wally," you might say, "college is expensive." That's very true. To go to college, you might have to take out student loans. And didn't Wally just get done telling you that debt was bad?

Bad debt is bad. But there is such a thing as good debt. Student loans are very good debt.

Here's why. Even if you spend $100,000 paying back your student loans, you will still make $800,000 more than if you didn't borrow that money.

**Student loan debt makes you money.
Credit card debt costs you money.**

Can you go to college without incurring debt? Yes. There are many ways of doing this. For example, does your employer offer tuition assistance? If the answer is yes, this may be a great way to save on tuition expenses.

Say you are 30 years old. Your employer offers tuition assistance, but you don't know if it's worth the effort. It could take five years of night school to get your degree. Is it worth it? You bet it is. **College grads earn about $25,000 more per year than high school grads.** If you plan to retire when you're 65, you have 30 more years to work after your five years of night school. Over those 30 more years, you will make about $25,000 more per year.

That's $750,000 more than you would have made without the degree.

Wally recommends that you think of tuition assistance this way. Your employer pays for your tuition, which itself costs tens of thousands of dollars. Then, when you graduate, you can earn an average of $25,000 more per year for the rest of your career. **A company that provides tuition reimbursement is a huge value to you. It can definitely help you find and grow your WOW! numbers.**

Another way to go to college without incurring debt is to earn scholarships. This is possible later in life, but it works best when you're still in high school.

Save $100,000 on Car Insurance

A student with a GPA of 3.0 or higher can receive up to 25% off of their auto insurance. A student saving $1,000 in insurance by age 19 would have 46 years to invest that money until age 65. At a 10% average annual return, this would turn into almost an extra $100,000 for their retirement. WOW!

If your high school grades are good enough, you have a chance of receiving scholarships and/or grants. **Scholarship money is more than a way to graduate without debt. It is a way to start building fairly amazing WOW! numbers.**

Let's say you work hard in high school. You get good grades. The result is scholarship money that pays for part of your college education.

If you didn't have a scholarship, you could graduate with $20,000 in student loans. At 4% interest over 10 years, that debt would cost you $202.50 per month.

Your good grades in high school got you a scholarship. Now, rather than paying off $20,000 in student loans, you graduate from college without debt.

Because you don't have to make a $202.50 loan payment every month, you can invest the money. Get a job with an employer who offers a 401(k) plan. Or, invest it in an IRA.

Even **without** employers matching funds, if you do this for 10 years (the typical payback period of a student loan) you would accumulate **$41,481** by the time you are 33 years old (at a 10% return). That's quite a WOW! number, just for getting good grades in high school. But as impressive as it is, it is only the beginning.

You already know WOW! numbers grow.
Imagine how a $41,481 WOW! number can grow.
Through the power of compounding interest, your
$41,481 turns into **$1,004,000** by the time you retire.

Imagine what it will feel like when you're 65. Your good grades in high school got you a scholarship. That scholarship saved you $202.50 per month. That money turned into a million dollar WOW! number by the time you retired.

Get Scholarship Information
*Go to **www.collegeanswer.com** to find scholarships and grants.*

Once you graduate, remember to turn them into WOW! numbers.

19

Knowing how to use a computer is a great way to make more money. The better your computer skills, the more likely you are to get a higher paying job. Just about any job in today's world requires some sort of computer skills. The more you know about computers and technology, the greater your chances of eventually getting a job with higher pay.

With the Internet, it is easier and cheaper than ever to get information. Yes, you can simply use the Internet to go shopping and post your blogs. Or, you can use it to become more knowledgeable. You can use it to develop your gold mind even further. Think about it. The Internet is like having thousands of libraries and newspapers right at your fingertips, overflowing with information to help better educate yourself, find your WOW! numbers and watch them grow.

An Attitude Adjustment

With so many ways to find your own personal gold mind, it's fair to ask, why isn't everybody rich? The problem isn't only people's debts, it's their attitudes.

Face it. These days, most people in our society just view debt as something that is just a part of their life. For many, it starts right out of high school. That's when we take out our first loan to pay for college. After we graduate, we enter the workforce already in debt with student loans. We get used to making a monthly payment on that debt and don't worry about it.

Now, as Wally told you before, student loan debt is good debt. That's not the trouble. The trouble begins when our attitude about good debt goes bad.

It starts when we take out loans for things we don't need. Debt for necessities (college) is not a bad thing. But debt for luxuries (plasma HD with surround sound) is a bad thing.

The problem is attitude. Our minds become immune to bad debt. We don't distinguish the difference between bad debt (luxuries) and good debt (necessities). Many of us simply see any type of debt as a way of life.

Wally Wow
Special Report

{PART 2}

Much of modern society has this bad attitude about debt. Many now use credit cards, retail financing and home equity without thinking twice. It gives them a false sense that they are spending less than they earn.

If your attitude about debt has gone bad, don't kid yourself. Don't get a false sense of security. The bad debt you take on is money that you owe. It will end up costing you dearly if you don't pay it off right away.

So, what can you do about it? **How can you change your attitude?** You have probably heard the saying, "You are the company you keep." To develop the attitudes of the financially wise, surround yourself with financially wise people. If you surround yourself with free spenders, then this is who you will be. If you surround yourself with frugal, responsible and thankful people, then that is who you will be.

Talk to your friends. Share this book with them. Support each other. Work on these things together. Instead of always going out to eat, take turns going to each others' houses. It will be cheaper. You will probably have just as much fun.

If you want to have more money, you need to develop a good attitude about bad debt. As Wally Wow would say, "You need an attitude adjustment."

The knowledge gained by reading this book helps you better manage your money. It allows you to get more out of your money. And just think: All you had to invest was the price of this book. **Knowledge doesn't always have to cost thousands of dollars in tuition expenses.**

Has this book paid for itself yet? Then you already broke even. But, the purpose of this book is not to help you break even, or even double or triple that.

> Wally Wow doesn't want to help
> you make peanuts. He wants to help
> you find your WOW! numbers.
> He wants you to invest them.
> He wants you to succeed.

Money Isn't Everything

Wally's definition of a valuable gold mind is not all about money. To be sure, it means being rich, but not just monetarily. Wally also wants you to be rich in character. He wants you to have good will towards others. He wants you to help others succeed by sharing what you know. He wants you to use what you know to be a positive influence on society. He wants you to live a life that is rich and full of meaning.

WOW!

CAUTION AHEAD

Do you want to cash in your WOW! numbers now, or "WOW!" them some more?

Then proceed slooooowly.

The following chapters are essential to maximizing the power of your WOW! numbers to completely **WOW! YOUR MONEY.**

Chapter 20
The Big Payoff

So far Wally focused most of his attention on saving and eliminating your debts. By doing these things, Wally showed you how to find WOW! numbers. He also told you what to do with them, once you find them. He described how they grow. He explained that when you retire, your WOW! numbers are an enormous nest egg. They're waiting for you: huge amounts of money, produced via the combination of money, time and compounding interest. Wally gave you great advice.

But do you want to know a little secret? It's not the greatest advice Wally has for you. No, that advice is yet to come. And it's not about saving money to build your nest egg to enormous proportions.

> It's about reducing living expenses so much that you don't need enormous amounts of money in order to retire comfortably.

Wally Wow
Special Report

Backwards Thinking

When you lower your expenses, you don't need as much money in retirement. If you have $3,500 per month in expenses, obviously you need more in your nest egg than if your expenses only total $2,500.

Most people make it a goal to have "x" amount in their retirement fund to cover their current expenses. Then they work towards accumulating that amount. This is better than no plan at all. As you know by now, Wally believes in saving for retirement.

But while it's good to save money for retirement, it is also smart to eliminate any expenses you can by the time you retire.

Pay off loans like your mortgage, car loan, home equity loan, credit cards, etc. before you retire. If these are paid off, you don't need your nest egg to cover them in the first place.

Your strategy should be to have $0 in debt expenses by retirement. Then you can look at how much it will take to cover ongoing expenses like electric, phone, cable, heat, food, entertainment, and so forth.

So stop backwards thinking. Pay off your expenses. Go forward!

20

To see why this is true, let's look at your mortgage.

Let's say you have a mortgage of $250,000 at a 6% interest rate. Your payment is $1,500 per month. If you are like most Americans, you pay taxes on your income. So, to pay your $1,500 mortgage each month, you have to earn, on average, about $2,083 (based on a 28% tax bracket).

Over the course of a year, it will take about $25,000 of your salary to cover the cost of your mortgage.

Now let's say you have $500,000 in an investment account. It is earning 5% annually. That would generate an annual return of $25,000. It would give you the income needed to pay your $1,500 mortgage each month on your $250,000 house.

But what if, instead of having a mortgage payment each month, you pay it off by the time you retire? If your mortgage is paid off, **you don't need to use $500,000 of your nest egg to generate the income needed to pay your mortgage**.

As you can now clearly see, paying off your mortgage really pays. Having a $250,000 house paid for is the same as having $500,000 in a retirement account. $250,000 equals $500,000?

So, as Wally just showed you, eliminating $1,500 of monthly mortgage expense is the same as having $500,000 in a retirement fund. If it works for mortgages, it should work for other expenses as well.

Let's say you have two car payments of $500 and $300, a credit card payment of $200, a home equity loan of $250 and a boat payment of $250. These add up to another $1,500 per month.

20

Guess what?

That means you need another $500,000 in your nest egg to cover these expenses.

But what if all of these expenses are paid off before you retire? **Paying off $3,000 in monthly expenses saves you $1,000,000.** If you don't pay off your debt, you need $1,000,000 to generate the income required to make the $3,000 payments each month. **So not owing $3,000 of monthly debt expenses is the same as having $1,000,000 in your nest egg.**

Think of it this way. $500,000 in a nest egg, with no expenses, is the same as $1,500,000 in a nest egg and $3,000 in monthly expenses.

Paying off your expenses by the time you retire is very smart, indeed.

You Don't Have To Wait

In this chapter, we're talking about eliminating expenses before you retire. That's a good goal, to be sure. Wally encourages everybody to do this. But he also wants you to remember that you don't have to wait.

If eliminating expenses by retirement is a good thing, eliminating them 10 years before you retire is a great thing. Eliminating them even earlier in life is even better. Take a look at your life. Look at all of your expenses. Ask yourself, "What can I eliminate?" You don't have to wait!

The amount you need in your retirement nest egg is directly proportionate to the expenses it needs to cover.

When you eliminate an expense, it means your nest egg no longer needs to cover the costs of that expense.

Baby Boomers and Monthly Expenses

If you plan to retire soon, like many Baby Boomers, you may think that it's too late to save. But there is hope. If you have a lot of monthly expenses, start getting rid of them now. As you've seen in this chapter, eliminating expenses is a guaranteed way to save. It greatly reduces the amount of income you need in retirement.

20

It doesn't take a lot of cash to eliminate expenses. Look at what paying just $25 extra each month on your mortgage can do.

By paying just **$25 extra** each month on a $250,000 mortgage, you **save $15,191** and pay it off **1 year and 3 months early**.

Look, on the next page, at what happens when you pay **$100 extra** each month. **You save over $50,000** and almost **5 years** worth of mortgage payments.

Paying $100 extra towards your mortgage each month is a **guaranteed** return to you that you will save $50,000. It is a guaranteed way to get you 5 years closer to eliminating a big expense at retirement.

Best of all, that's an expense that your nest egg will no longer need to cover.

The table, below, shows how much you can save by paying extra on your 30-year mortgage each month.

Loan Amount	Pay Extra	You'll Save	Reduce MTG By Years / Months
$250,000 6% Interest	$25	$15,191	1 / 03
	$50	$28,662	2 / 06
	$75	$40,713	3 / 07
	$100	$51,572	4 / 06
	$150	$70,409	6 / 03
	$200	$86,232	7 / 09
	$250	$99,750	9 / 00
	$300	$111,459	10 / 01
	$400	$130,782	12 / 00
	$500	$146,128	13 / 07
	$750	$173,665	16 / 05
	$1,000	$192,086	18 / 04
	$1,500	$215,349	20 / 11
	$2,000	$229,512	22 / 07

Somebody once challenged Wally by saying, "I don't want to pay off my mortgage early. It's my only tax deduction." To that Wally replied, "Would you give somebody a dollar for 25 cents?"

Yes, tax deductions are good. But paying off expenses is better. If you are worried about losing out on mortgage interest you can deduct from your taxes, don't be.

When you pay down your mortgage, you will probably find you get back $2 - $4 for each $1 you pay extra on the principal. If you are in the 15-35% tax bracket, the government will likely give you back 15-35 cents for every dollar you pay in mortgage interest. So, the obvious thing to do is pay the mortgage off early. Forego the 15-35 cents return on your dollar from the government. Instead, get a $2-$4 return on your dollar by paying off your mortgage expense.

20

Use Automatic Withdrawal to Win

Set up an automatic amount to be deducted and paid on your mortgage. Doing this ensures you do not spend the money somewhere else.

Clearly, paying off your expenses before retirement is great advice, perhaps the greatest advice Wally has given. You don't need to generate any income to cover expenses you don't have. You will be much better off in retirement when your nest egg doesn't have to go toward expenses. By paying off your expenses before retirement, you win.

It's the big payoff, and it's all yours.

Chapter 21
The Inflation Equalizer
(Your American Dream)

 Since the beginning, across the generations of the United States of America, home ownership has been the biggest aspect of the "American Dream." From our country's earliest days, through the settling of the frontier and to this very day, owning our homes is important to us. It's one of our nation's greatest strengths. It is also ironic.

Home ownership is ironic because it is part of the American dream, and also a big reason why many Americans achieve it. You might be saying, "How can this be? How can owning a home be part of the dream, as well as a way to get the dream in the first place?" It is a puzzle, to be sure. But fortunately, it's a puzzle Wally can piece together for us.

You see, there are two big hurdles facing all of us in retirement. They are:

- Inflation
- Housing Costs

Inflation is a huge threat. What happens if we save money all our lives, only to find out it wasn't enough? We work and save all of those years, only to find out that prices have gone up? Suddenly, with inflation, we can't afford to do the things we planned to do.

**Inflation is the arch-enemy
of your WOW! numbers.**

Inflation is bad enough on its own. However, it has a sidekick that's just as nasty.

Like inflation, housing costs are also a threat to our retirement.

Having enough money to cover housing costs is important. It is clearly something to plan for long before we retire. However, if housing costs increase when our income is fixed, it is clearly a problem.

Now, here's where the irony comes in. Remember, owning a home is a big part of the American dream. So, how do you achieve the American dream? If you just said, "By owning a home," Wally salutes you!

That's right. It is true. The secret to neutralizing inflation is the same as the secret to controlling housing costs. That secret is home ownership.

Buying a home and having it paid for by retirement allows you to clear both of these significant retirement hurdles.

Home ownership, in a house paid for by the time you retire, eliminates one of your biggest monthly expenses (housing). Whenever you eliminate an expense, it makes your WOW! numbers go further.

You might be thinking, "But Wally, if I find and invest my WOW! numbers, a house payment won't be a big deal." Perhaps you are right. But remember, whatever you manage to save has to go a long way in retirement. You want to be able to enjoy the fruits of your labor. Without the added expense of a house payment, you stand a much better chance of doing so.

> ### Here's why inflation is such a threat. Do you think a million bucks is a lot? Today it is! But with inflation, 30 years from now it will have the equivalent purchasing power of only about $400,000. This is due to inflation.

When estimating how much you need in your retirement nest egg, $1 million usually sounds pretty nice. Certainly most people don't shoot for just $400,000. That simply is not enough for most people. If they live for 20 years after retirement, $400,000 only gives them $20,000 per year to live on. If they have a $1,000 per month house payment, it is worse. Then, they only have $8,000 per year to cover everything else. You need to plan for inflation today, in order to live your American dream later. Your nest egg needs to be large enough to fund the price of goods when you retire, not now.

"Wouldn't it be nice if hamburgers still only cost a couple of quarters?"

Yes, it would be great to pay the early 1970's prices of 50 cents for a burger, $1 for a movie ... 45 cents for a gallon of gas. At those prices even a $100,000 retirement fund sounded great in 1975. But as you know, the price of burgers, gas, movies and everything else went up. Trust Wally on this one. You won't be paying today's prices in 2015, 2030, 2040, or any other year in the future.

> At the historical average inflation
> rate of 3%, the $1 million you think
> you need today will have to
> equal $2,427,262 in 30 years.
> An easy way to think of it is to
> simply multiply by 2.5.

21

Say you plan to retire 30 years from now. You plan to have $1 million by then. Your WOW! numbers are invested. They are compounding. With $1 million in the bank, you think that you will have enough to retire in style.

That may be true, but please remember to plan for inflation. Multiply the amount you think you need by 2.5.

At 3% inflation, 30 years from now, you will need $2.5 million in order to live as if you had $1 million today.

The table below shows how this works. It covers time periods from 5 to 40 years.

The Effects of Inflation

Based on a 3% Annual Inflation Rate
Amount of money you'll need in:

Today's Value	5 Years	10 Years	20 Years	30 Years	40 Years
$25,000	$28,982	$33,598	$45,153	$60,682	$81,551
$50,000	$57,964	$67,196	$90,306	$121,363	$163,102
$100,000	$115,927	$134,392	$180,611	$242,726	$326,204
$200,000	$231,855	$268,783	$361,222	$485,452	$652,408
$500,000	$579,637	$671,958	$903,056	$1,213,631	$1,631,019
$1,000,000	$1,159,274	$1,343,916	$1,806,111	$2,427,262	$3,262,038
$2,000,000	$2,318,548	$2,687,833	$3,612,222	$4,854,525	$6,524,076

As you can see, with 3% inflation, it doesn't take long to pay much more for something. **That is why home ownership is so important.**

Perhaps you rent your home today. The payments are reasonable. You also don't have to worry about home maintenance, lawn care and so forth. Those are definite pluses. But while renting can be convenient, it is far more expensive than you may think. What's worse, while you can lock in a house payment for 30 years, rent payments rise as time goes by.

Rents rise because property values go up. **Historically, property values have increased at about 5% annually.**

This means that a $250,000 home will likely be worth $1.75 million in 40 years.

21

If you are renting a $250,000 home today, paying about **$1,500 per month**, how much do you think you'll pay when that home is worth $1.75 million?

How does $10,500 per month sound?
($1,500 at a 5% historical annual increase will become about $10,500 in 40 years.)

That's right. Inflation makes rent go up, just like everything else. **But, if you buy a home and pay for it before you retire, two things happen:**

- Your payment stays the same throughout the term of your mortgage.
- Your home's value increases.

Wally Wow
Special Report

Historical Housing Values
New Single-Family Median Home Prices: 1963-1996

Period	Price	Period	Price	Period	Price
1963	$18,000	1975	$39,300	1987	$104,500
1964	$18,900	1976	$44,200	1988	$112,500
1965	$20,000	1977	$48,800	1989	$120,000
1966	$21,400	1978	$55,700	1990	$122,900
1967	$22,700	1979	$62,900	1991	$120,000
1968	$24,700	1980	$64,600	1992	$121,500
1969	$25,600	1981	$68,900	1993	$126,500
1970	$23,400	1982	$69,300	1994	$130,000
1971	$25,200	1983	$75,300	1995	$133,900
1972	$27,600	1984	$79,900	1996	$140,000
1973	$32,500	1985	$84,300		
1974	$35,900	1986	$92,000		

Sources: Bureau of the Census, Department of Commerce; and Office of Policy Development and Research, Department of Housing and Urban Development

As you can see from the table above, from 1963-1996 the median price of a house increased nearly 6% annually. This excludes the housing boom after 1996.

If housing prices continue to rise at only a 5% annual rate, a $250,000 house today will cost over $1.75 million in 40 years. The mortgage payment for this house, assuming a 30-year loan, at a 6% interest rate, will be $10,500 per month.

Owning a home is clearly your inflation equalizer.

- It eliminates your biggest monthly expense in retirement.
- It prevents inflation from stealing your WOW! numbers.

Rent goes up in cost through the years. A mortgage payment stays the same.

By purchasing a home and paying for it by retirement, you reduce your monthly "rent" payment to $0. Compare that to the $10,500 per month in rent you might otherwise be paying 40 years from now.

21

Home Buying Tips

You can see how important it is to buy into the American dream. But Wally is a realist. He knows that now may not be the right time for you to own a home. You may be better off waiting for a short time.

Important things to consider before you buy include:

• If you have no idea where you want to live 2 or 3 years from now, you might not want to buy a home yet.

• Closing costs on a home can cost thousands of dollars. If you move just a couple of years later, the price of your home may not increase enough to cover these costs.

• Ask yourself if you really want to own a single-family home. Is a condo or townhouse a better choice for you? It takes time and money to maintain a single-family home. Are you physically able to do the work? A condo or townhouse may be a great alternative.

• If you plan on using an Adjustable Rate Mortgage to finance your home, make certain you can pay the maximum interest rate in the future if mortgage rates rise. Don't get lured in by low rates today, only to find that you can't make the payments in the future.

• Beware of "interest only" loans. Chances are you are not ready to own a home if you need to go this route.

Wally Wow
Special Report

{PART 2}

A good way to see if you're ready for home ownership is to pretend that you already own a house. Find out what the mortgage payments would be, plus expenses such as real estate taxes, mortgage insurance, repairs and maintenance, and so on. Set aside money each month for sewer, water, gas, garbage, heat, and repairs. Know these costs so you can get an accurate estimate of your total housing expenses. Do this for at least 3 months.

By shifting your spending, you may find you do have the money to own a home right now. If you can keep up with the pretend payments, then you are probably ready to own a house. And since you actually set aside money each month, you even have money to put towards a down payment on your house.

On the other hand, you may learn that now isn't a good time to buy. You can't afford the payments. Putting aside that much money each month made you feel uneasy. If that's the case, then owning a house isn't a good idea at this time.

If you learn that it's not a good time to buy, don't worry. The time will come. When it does, the important thing is to be ready for it.

One way to get ready for home ownership is to reduce your debt load.

21

For example: Let's say Wally has a monthly $250 car payment. He also has a credit card payment of $300. Together, Wally is paying $550 per month toward debt. The obvious result of paying the debt is that Wally has $550 less cash per month. **The not so obvious result is that the bank will now loan Wally $550 less per month when he needs the money to buy his house.**

So what can Wally do? The simple answer is that he can, and should, eliminate his debt. Simply getting rid of the credit card debt qualifies Wally for $300 more per month. Mortgage companies use formulas that compare the amount of debt you have to the amount of money you make. By reducing and eliminating as much debt as possible, you will qualify for a larger mortgage.

The table, below, shows how this works.

Interest Rate	Loan Amount 30-Year Mortgage				
	$150,000	$200,000	$250,000	$300,000	$350,000
5%	$805.23	$1,073.64	$1,342.05	$1,610.46	$1,878.88
6%	$899.33	$1,199.10	$1,498.88	$1,798.65	$2,098.43
7%	$997.95	$1,330.60	$1,663.26	$1,995.91	$2,328.56
8%	$1,100.65	$1,467.53	$1,834.41	$2,201.29	$2,568.18
9%	$1,206.93	$1,609.25	$2,011.56	$2,413.87	$2,816.18

As you can see, $300 per month qualifies you for a larger mortgage. Specifically, with **$300 less debt per month** and a 6% mortgage loan interest rate, you qualify for **$50,000** more.

Paying a mortgage is like depositing money in a 401(k).

Think about it. Over 40 years of inflation, your rent increases. At a 5% increase, it goes from $1,500 a month to $10,500. This equals $126,000 per year.

Assume you are in the 28% tax bracket. That means you need $175,000 in income to pay $126,000.

Where do you get the money? Do you want to withdraw from your principal? If not, you need a $3,500,000 nest egg. At a 5% annual return, it takes a $3,500,000 nest egg to produce $175,000 in interest. ($3,500,000 X 5% = $175,000)

21

With a mortgage, your monthly house payment stays at $1,500.

In essence, your mortgage produced $3,500,000. That's money your 401(k) would otherwise have to produce.

A mortgage is what keeps you from needing millions more in a retirement account. Your mortgage is your inflation equalizer. It is an extension of your 401(k).

Stake your claim on America!

If you've been paying attention, by now you are most likely convinced. Home ownership truly is the inflation equalizer, and the key to your American dream. By paying for your home before you retire, you are, in essence, contributing to a very powerful savings plan. Best of all, your return on investment is guaranteed. Buying a house today, or as soon as you are ready, protects your WOW! numbers and reduces the amount of money you need in retirement. Remember, it's your American dream!

Chapter 22
Investing Made Easy

In recent years, primarily because of the Internet, the ability of ordinary Americans to invest has grown enormously. Today, with little training or experience, people go online to buy and sell stocks every day. They also invest online in many other ways, including:

- Commodities (gold, grain, diamonds, pork bellies, etc.)
- Collectibles (antique cars, cuckoo clocks, dolls, etc.)
- Futures markets (betting prices will rise or fall on any number of items)
- Gambling (lottery tickets, horse racing, sports wagering and online poker)

There are literally thousands of investment possibilities. The number of opportunities to invest is so large it can be hard to know where to start.

22

Wally says, **"It doesn't have to be so complicated."** You can make your WOW! numbers grow, by following Wally's straightforward advice. In fact, by avoiding the complexity, you stand a much better chance of success.

Remember, you only need to average 10%. Throughout this book, you've seen Wally use 10% when calculating returns from your WOW! numbers. It's likely that you've asked yourself, "Where does Wally get 10% returns?" After all, most savings accounts offer far less than that these days, right?

In this chapter, in addition to many other things, Wally shows you a simple formula to average 10%. By the time you've finished reading this section of the book, you too will know how to turn your WOW! numbers into the kind of cash you need for retirement.

Before Wally gets started, it's useful to refresh our memory as to why 10% is so important. Look at the table, below. It shows the returns over 40 years from a $10 per day (or $300 per month) investment. Notice the dramatic difference between 5% and 10%? As shown earlier in this book, although you think 10% is only twice as much as 5%, you end up with much more than twice the money.

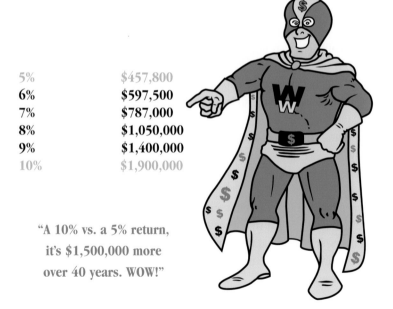

5%	$457,800
6%	$597,500
7%	$787,000
8%	$1,050,000
9%	$1,400,000
10%	$1,900,000

"A 10% vs. a 5% return,
it's $1,500,000 more
over 40 years. WOW!"

To increase your return on investment, you need to know where to go for higher returns. **There are many possible places to invest your money.** Savings accounts are one option. Other options include:

Stocks
- Large Cap
- Small Cap
- International

Bonds
- U.S. Government
- Corporate
- Municipal

Money Market Funds
- Treasury Bills
- Commercial Paper
- Bank Certificates of Deposit (CDs)

22

Over the years, each of these types of investments has produced
different average yields. Look at the chart, below. It shows the average
yields for each of the various investment types. The average yields shown
are based on tracking that goes back all the way to 1926.

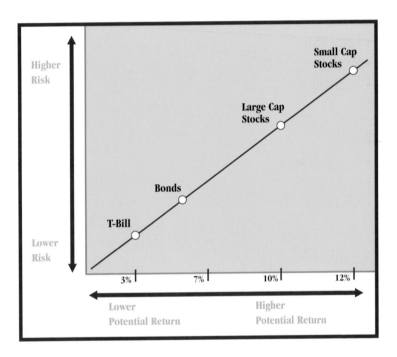

As you can see, across all investment types, **greater possible risk offers a greater possible return.** This is how investing works. **Stocks** are riskier than bonds. If they didn't offer a better possible return, nobody would invest in them. **Bonds** are more risky than treasury bills, so the average return from bond investments is higher. For all types of investments, the rule is:

Greater possible risk

=

Greater possible return

It's very important to note the word **"possible."** Wally wants you to know that stocks can return more than bonds. However, he also wants you to know that there are **no guarantees.** People do lose money in the stock market. You can lose money in the stock market, as well. You can also lose money in other investments. Across all investments, there are associated risks.

22

Wally Wow
Special Report

Farmers, Eggs and Baskets

The word "diversify" is just a fancy way of saying:

"Don't put all your eggs in one basket."

That's an old-fashioned saying, from back in the days when farmers went out every morning to collect eggs. They used baskets to carry them. Of course, from time-to-time, a basket would be dropped. If all the eggs were in one basket, they all broke. So, farmers learned to put a portion of their eggs in one basket, a portion in another, and so on. The lesson they learned hundreds of years ago, about carrying eggs, applies to investing today.

To minimize your risk, you need to diversify your investments.
There are three ways to diversify risk. They are:

1. Diversify your selections of stocks.

This is the "farmers and eggs" approach. If you have your money in ten stocks rather than one, you won't lose all your money if that one stock goes belly up.

2. Buy stocks in different industries and sectors of the market.

If you buy ten stocks in oil and the world discovers a new, cheaper energy source, all ten of your oil stocks will probably go down. Alternatively, if you spread your investments out in financials, technology, transportation, etc. those stocks won't be affected. In fact, if oil stocks go down, the others might gain value. This is because those companies won't have to spend as much for fuel costs, and thus are more profitable.

22

3. Give yourself more time.

The table on the next page helps to explain what Wally means here. S&P 500® is a registered trademark of McGraw-Hill Companies, Inc. It shows the range of compounded annual returns for the S&P 500 Index for varying holding periods from 1926-2005. The S&P 500 is an index of 500 large capital common stocks. It is widely used as an indicator of the broader market.

Large Cap Stocks		
Holding Periods	High Return	Low Return
1 Year	53.9%	-43.3%
5 Year	28.6%	-12.5%
10 Year	20.1%	-0.9%
20 Year	17.9%	3.1%

Average Historical Return (1926-2005) **10.4%**

Do you see what Wally means by giving yourself more time? Across one year of large cap stocks, the historic high return was 53.9%. But the historic low return was -43.3%. If you invest in large cap stocks for 20 years, the historic high return drops to 17.9%, but the historic low return actually increases to +3.1%. So since 1926, even the very worst 20-year time period still returned an average gain of 3.1%. This includes the depression era.

Across the 80 years from 1926 to 2005, the average return on the S&P 500 large cap stock index was 10.4%.

With the possibility of large losses, you may not want to invest in stocks as you near retirement. At age 55 you don't want to lose 43% of your nest egg, right? As shown in the table, that could happen. **If you are 55 and want to retire in 10 years, you can't afford to take the risks that you could take when you were 25.** You can still invest, however. You just need to do it in less risky ways.

When you diversify your investments, you are "asset allocating." This is a fancy way of saying, again, that you're not putting all of your eggs in one basket. The key to asset allocation is to adjust the mix, as you get older.

Wally knows that there are lots of people out there who want to tell you how to allocate your assets. Many, as discussed in earlier chapters, are reputable. They give great advice. Some even give it at a reasonable cost. You can listen to them, if you like. You can pay them, if you like. Or, you can let Wally give you some good recommendations on how to allocate your assets, by reading the paragraphs below.

The table, below, shows the blend of stocks, fixed income, and money market funds that should make up your investment portfolio at different points in your life.

	20 or more years until retirement	10 to 20 years until retirement	0 to 10 years until retirement
Aggressive			
Stocks	100	80-100	50-70
Fixed Income	0	10-20	40-60
Money Market	0	0	0-20

Moderate			
Stocks	70-90	50-70	30-50
Fixed Income	10-20	15-30	40-70
Money Market	0-10	0-20	0-30

Conservative			
Stocks	60-80	40-60	15-30
Fixed Income	20-40	15-35	40-70
Money Market	0-20	0-30	25-40

22

As you can see from the table, you shift assets away from stocks as you get closer to retirement. Again, this is because you don't want to chance hitting a "down" year, when you only have a few years left to invest. When you are younger, stocks are a good place to invest. If they go down for a year or even two, it's not a big deal when you're 25 years old. At that point in your life, it's a good bet that you have time to recover from your losses. However, as shown in the table, you should allocate your assets differently, as you near retirement.

The table also shows three typical investment strategies:

- Conservative
- Moderate
- Aggressive

These strategies are less about finance than they are about personality. All of us are different. We all have different personalities. For example, you may be the kind of person who enjoys ski jumping, or mountain climbing, or parachuting. If that's you, then a moderate or even aggressive investment strategy might be right for you. If you like less risky activities, then a more conservative investment strategy might be the one you follow. However, whatever your comfort level with risk happens to be, moving away from stocks as you near retirement is a good idea.

"But Wally," you may be thinking, "how on earth do I figure out which stocks to invest in? There are too many and I don't know where to begin." That's a good question. The answer for you may be mutual funds, possibly in the form of index funds.

Mutual funds are one of the best ways for almost all people to invest. They exist because the stock market is complex. It is too hard for most people to do all of the research required. Most people don't know enough about business, economics and the stock market to make good decisions. But mutual fund companies know a lot about all of those things, and much more. By investing in mutual funds, you stand a much better chance of making the right investment decisions.

You still need to pick the right mutual funds, of course. With so many out there (thousands of them) this can be as complex as picking individual stocks themselves. Wally has good advice for you here. Look for a fund that averaged a high return over many years. By high return, Wally means at least the broad market average (i.e. the S&P 500 index). By many years, Wally means at least 10 years.

> If in the last 10 years a mutual
> fund has not returned the market average
> (i.e. the S&P 500 index),
> **Wally says, "Find a different fund."**

22

It's also wise to steer clear of short-term results. For example, don't invest in a fund, just because it earned 30% last year. There are always funds that do well for a short period of time. But, no fund does well all of the time.

Wally's point is that it is virtually impossible to predict when a fund will return 30%, or possibly lose 30%. The average return for stocks over the history of the S&P 500 index is 10.4%. To make all of your WOW! numbers grow as shown in other sections of this book, however, you only need to average 10%. Let your WOW! numbers grow by investing them in a solid mutual or index fund. Look for average returns of 10% over 10 years or more.

Historically, another good way to earn 10% or more is to choose an index fund. These are also sometimes called "exchange traded funds (ETF)." The stocks that make up these types of funds represent leading companies that are traded on a particular exchange, or are found within a particular group of regularly measured stocks. For example, an index fund might be made up of leading stocks from the New York Stock Exchange (NYSE). It might be made up of stocks from the NASDAQ exchange. It could also be made up of stocks from the Dow or S&P 500 indexes.

Index fund managers are paid to ensure that their funds match or exceed the performance of the exchange or index they follow. Every day, as you may already know, results are reported from the leading exchanges and indexes. The index fund managers pay careful attention to these reports. They adjust their funds to match the performance of the exchanges and indexes.

While index or ETF funds don't always generate the highest returns, they are historically consistent.

In fact, funds based on the S&P 500 have returned an average of over 10% a year since 1926.

Investing in an S&P index fund doesn't guarantee you a 10% return this year, or even across the next five years. It does, however, provide a high level of confidence that you may average a 10% return or better across 10 years or more.

Whether you invest on your own, or utilize a mutual fund, **you will pay fees in order to invest.** These fees will vary. Your goal, of course, is to pay the least amount possible.

Today, there are many companies that offer low investment fees. Wally recommends that you do some research before you invest. Ask questions. Make sure that you are getting the best possible deal.

For example, one investment firm might say that they only charge 2% per transaction. Another might have a flat fee per transaction. Another might charge a flat fee for a certain time period. It can be confusing. You have to do some math to figure out which deal is best.

Once you find an investment firm that charges reasonable fees (lower than the other places you investigate), it's time to allocate your assets. Again, there are many ways to do this. However, since the index funds have good track records, a simple approach is to invest the stock portion of your portfolio in an **S&P 500 index fund.** Historically, it has been about the best thing you can do with your money.

Wally says…

"The S&P 500 is one of my top picks."

22

Allocate the rest of your money in a high quality treasury bond fund, or a money market account. If you reference the asset allocation chart, on page 197, you can see which to choose based on your current age.

> **With a proven mutual or index fund, and either a treasury bond or money market fund, you have set up a diversified portfolio. That's not hard, is it?**

Wally says…

"That's all there is to it!"

Now, Wally knows that there are thousands of possible ways to invest. You can buy gold. You can buy other commodities. You can spend every waking moment online trading and researching and investing and trading and researching and … but you don't have to make it that complicated. Investing doesn't have to be hard. Investing can be easy. Simply follow Wally's advice and make your WOW! numbers grow. That's all there is to it.

Chapter 23
Protecting Your WOW! Numbers

Do you know what an "actuary" is? An actuary is a person who calculates risk. Insurance companies hire actuaries. They pay them to figure out the risk involved with almost every part of life. To figure out these risks, they study mountains of data. They apply complex mathematics. The result of their work is a very accurate estimate of the risk associated with almost any activity, including life itself.

It's mostly because of actuaries that we know things like "how long men live" and "how long women live" and "how many 18-year-old males will have car accidents this year" (the answer is "lots of them"). Across the body of their work, actuaries provide guidance for insurance companies, to be sure. They also provide guidance for the rest of us.

For example, actuaries know that there is a very good chance you will be around for your 65th birthday.

Statistically speaking, you have a 75% chance of living until age 65.

23

After that, the average life expectancy for men is 82 years and for women it's 85. Knowing this is important. It helps you figure out not only how long you have to live, but how much money you'll need, in order to live that long.

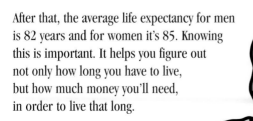

Will you have enough? Will your WOW! numbers grow until you retire? Will your retirement nest egg last 17 or 20 or more years? In the previous chapters of this book, Wally showed you how to find your WOW! numbers. He showed you how to invest them and make them grow. Now, in this chapter, he shows you how to protect them.

The key to making your WOW! numbers grow, as you hopefully recall, is you. The key to protecting your WOW! numbers, as you soon will see, is insurance.

Purchasing proper amounts of insurance is critically important to your financial success. Think how devastating it would be to lose your WOW! numbers. What a tragedy it would be to do everything right (all that you learned in the rest of this book) only to lose your WOW! numbers because you didn't insure them.

There are many forms of insurance that you need, including:

- Life
- Long-Term Care
- Health & Dental
- Home Owners or Renters
- Auto

It's easy to get overwhelmed by the many types, varieties, costs and so on. But have no fear. **Just as Wally made investing easy in the previous chapter, he makes insurance easy in the pages to come.**

Let's start by looking at life insurance. The first question you need to answer is, **"Do I need it?"**

The answer is easy to figure out. If you have anybody who depends on your income, whether a spouse, child, parent or any other person, then the answer is "yes." If you have any kind of dependent(s), you need life insurance. If you don't have any dependents, then you do not need life insurance.

If the answer to "do I need it" is "yes," then the next question is naturally, **"How much do I need?"**

This is also an easy question to answer. Most experts recommend that your life insurance equal 10-20 times the amount your dependents need in order to support themselves without you. In any case, make sure it is enough for your dependents to support themselves.

Now let's look at long-term care insurance. **Do you need it?**

The answer is again simple. Most people in their 50s need it. If you are in your 50s, add a long-term care policy to your insurance coverage. This provides you with a payout to cover nursing home costs as well as a variety of in-home health care expenses.

How much long-term care insurance do you need?

23

The average stay in a nursing home is about three years. To play it safe, purchase a policy that covers up to four years of nursing home care.

What about health and dental insurance? Do you need it? The answer is "yes."

Everybody needs health insurance.
Everybody should consider dental insurance.

How much do you need?

The simple answer is, as much as you can afford. This is one area in which you do not want to skimp. Many people have lost all of their life savings, their WOW! numbers, because of health care bills.

If your employer offers health care insurance, you will need to calculate the cost of the premium, deductible, and maximum out-of-pocket expenses to determine which plan is right for you.

For dental insurance, it may or may not be cost effective depending on the cost of your premium.

If you cannot get health and/or dental insurance through your employer, you should contact your state's insurance department to get options. Small business owners and self-employed persons should join a professional or trade organization that offers discounted group rates. This usually costs more than if you were employed by somebody else, but it is necessary. If you can't join a professional or trade organization, contact your local insurance agent for options and rates.

What about home owners or renters insurance? **Do you need it?**

Yes, everybody needs it.

How much do you need?

You need enough to replace all your possessions if something were to happen. Make sure your home or renters insurance includes a provision for Unlimited Additional Living Expense coverage (UALE). This coverage pays for additional costs if you need to move into temporary housing due to your home being damaged or destroyed. If you only have "limited coverage" you run the risk that your money will run out before you're back in your home.

How about auto insurance? **Do you need it?**

If you own a car, the answer is yes. This is not only because it makes financial sense, but also because almost everywhere, it is the law.

There are many types of auto insurance that you need. For liability, uninsured motorist, property damage, etc. Wally recommends that you buy the legal minimums. Requirements differ from state to state, but your insurance agent will know what these amounts are. For collision and/or "comprehensive" coverage, the key is to pay the least amount possible.

You do this by increasing the "deductible" payment associated with your collision or comprehensive coverage. The "deductible" is the amount of money that you have to pay, yourself, if your car is damaged.

23

For example, let's say Wally is driving along one fine winter day and hits a patch of ice. His car spins out of control, and he smashes into a guard rail. The estimate to repair his car is $2,495. His auto insurance policy has a $500 deductible. Wally has to pay the $500 himself. The insurance company will only pay $1,995.

Your goal is to buy the highest deductible amount possible. Doing so lowers your insurance premium. To do this, simply figure out how much you could afford to pay, out-of-pocket, if you had to repair your car.

If you can cover a $1,000 deductible, this is the type of policy you should buy. A $1,000 deductible versus a $500 or $250 can save you a lot of money per month. If the $1,000 deductible only saves you $50 per month, it's worth it. **As you know by now,** $50 per month **is quite a WOW! number.**

In addition to the types of insurance outlined, above, you may need four additional types of "insurance." These aren't policies, per se, but rather, ways you protect yourself and your family through legal means. They include:

- Advanced Directive and Durable Power of Attorney for Health Care
- Revocable Trust
- Will
- Durable Financial Power of Attorney

You should have any of these documents if you are concerned about who inherits your estate upon your death or incapacitation.

It Pays to Pay for Good Legal Advice

All of these documents are typically prepared by attorneys. While you can purchase forms and templates online and at book stores, Wally recommends that you pay the reasonable fee attorneys charge to prepare such documents. In many states, the legal issues addressed by these documents are tricky. When you need the protection these documents provide for you and your family, it will be too late to rewrite them properly.

If you do not prepare these, it will be left up
to the courts. Do you want the courts
deciding who has the right to your
money and possessions?

> ### Save it for a rainy day.
> *You've heard the saying, "save it for a rainy day," right?
> That's how savings accounts should be used, for the rainy
> days we all have in life. We lose a job. We accidentally break
> something valuable. We live normal lives, and from time to
> time need a little extra money to get by. That's what savings
> accounts are for.*

Your **savings account** is essentially your **"everything else"
insurance. It is your financial insurance.** It is a fund that pays you,
yourself, if something unexpected happens. It covers circumstances that
the other insurances Wally just talked about do not cover.

Yes, you can reject Wally and ignore the need for a savings account. Just
like health, auto, homeowners, or life insurance, if you are fortunate,
you never need a savings account, either. But obviously, you never know
if you will actually need to use it or not. And if you do need it, a savings
account can help you avoid financial disaster.

For Wally, a reasonable savings account is a case of "it's better to be safe
than sorry." As with any other insurance, the consequence of not having
it is significant when something happens and you don't have it. In
uncertain times and unstable job markets, an emergency savings
account is very good insurance, indeed.

23

So how much should you keep in your savings account? Most experts recommend 3-9 months worth of emergency money. But no matter what the experts say, Wally recommends that you put enough into a bank account to make you feel comfortable and free of worries. If that means you save more than other people, then put in more money.

To review, Wally showed you how to grow your WOW! numbers in the other chapters of this book. In this chapter, using many forms of insurance, he showed you how to protect your WOW! numbers. **Both are necessary for your financial success.**

Actuarially speaking, you are 100% more likely to succeed when you both grow and protect your WOW! numbers.

Chapter 24
The WOW! Life

If you're reading this, it's likely that you've already read the previous chapters. Has it made you think? Has it made you change your ways? Are you finding and building WOW! numbers yet? Are you doing what it takes to live a WOW! life?

"Live for the WOW!"

Wally certainly hopes so. More than anything, he wants to help you find, grow and protect your WOW! numbers. It's an uncertain world, but as you've seen in this book, you can control a lot. This doesn't have to be hard, either. Simply follow Wally's advice and you can live the WOW! life of your dreams.

Take time to work for yourself each day. Approach this work as the CEO of your own **multi-million dollar** business. As you know by now, that's really what you are. By acting like it, you can retire with the money you need to not only survive your golden years, but thrive during them. You can also have a lot more money to enjoy today, as well.

24

Wally Wow has shown you many ways to achieve your goals. By finding your own personal treasure, paying down your debts and developing your gold mind, you now have what it takes to succeed. Doing these things will generate WOW! numbers. Put them in the right places by buying into your American dream. Pay off all your debts by retirement. Put your money in the right investments. Insure nothing happens to your WOW! numbers. These are the things Wally believes in. They are the keys to your financial independence. They are not impossible, or even very difficult.

So why don't more people follow Wally's advice? One reason is because this is Wally's first book. Most people haven't read it yet. Another reason, however, is more serious.

Unfortunately, most people say **"I can't"** too easily. They say it too quickly. They say it far too often. It becomes comfortable for them. It becomes a way of life. When faced with opportunities to excel, they retreat behind those two simple words: **"I can't."** Sadly, once you say **"I can't"** it is almost certain that **"you won't."**

The wealthiest people in the world never said, "I can't be a millionaire because I only make $30,000 a year." They didn't say, "I can't." Rather, they said, "I can. There must be a way." And guess what? They weren't satisfied until they found that way. Rather than resigning from life by saying "I can't do that," they challenged themselves by saying "I can do that! I can save. I can make more. I can find my WOW! numbers and help them grow."

Saying "I can't" is, plainly and simply, negative thinking. It is negative thinking that separates almost every successful person from every unsuccessful person. Yes, there are tragedies and unforeseen circumstances in life, but amazing, miraculous recovery is possible from any circumstance. "I can" paves the way for positive improvement, changed circumstances and innovation. There are always new and better ways to make your life better. Saying "I can" is one of those ways.

> Listen to any successful person, and they will preach to you determination, perseverance, and resilience. The bottom line is this: **never quit.**

There will always be new challenges. There will always be obstacles. There will always be circumstances that make the WOW! numbers seem impossible. Everyone faces hardship. Unexpected things happen in life. The difference between winners and losers is who overcomes and adjusts. If you fall, get back up. If you can't run, then walk. If you can't walk, then crawl. Successful people aren't immune to troubles. It's not that they never face hardship. When they do, however, they don't assume it's permanent.

24

Keep pressing on towards the goal. No one is perfect. Many mistakes will be made. The important thing is that you persevere. Move towards your goals. Keep building your WOW! numbers, no matter how many "bumps in the road" there may be along the way. Yes, there will be bumps, but you can make it. No matter what happens, as long as you keep going, as long as you don't quit, as long as you don't say, "I can't," you are never a failure.

Will you make mistakes? Absolutely. Everyone makes mistakes along the way. What matters most is not that you make mistakes, but rather what you learn from your mistakes. What you learn helps to make you a winner. When you get back up and move towards your goal, you can't help but end up crossing the line a winner. With Wally's help, and a good attitude, you will find your WOW! numbers, help them grow and retire far richer than you imagined possible.

Wally Wow
Special Report

The Truth Shall Set You Free

How you spend your money and what you spend your money on tells Wally a lot about you. What it doesn't tell him is if you can really afford it or not.

Are you creating a false financial impression? Do you spend money on things you know you can't afford? Do you do it just to impress other people? Do you try to make it appear like you have more money than you really do?

Credit cards are easy to get. They make it easy for you to live above your means. They make it easy to spend more than you actually make. They are a huge threat to your financial success.

Don't give in to the threat. Don't give in to your desires the moment you want something. That is what gets you into financial trouble. Rather than always wanting more, trying to get whatever is next, be patient. Be content. Be happy with what you have.

Perhaps you were once happy with a $10,000 car. Then you had to have a $20,000 car. That soon turned into a $30,000 car. Then it became a $40,000 car. **The more you made, the more you fulfilled your new desires. You always wanted more. You always tried to get it.**

24

Wally Wow *Special Report*

{PART 2}

That way of life is why some people who earn $5 million, $9 million or even $16 million and more end up not being able to retire. No matter how much they make, there is no end to fulfilling their desires. They were not true to themselves. They were not true with their money.

How truthful are you with your money? However you answer this question today, one thing is certain: sooner or later, the truth will be revealed. **Will your truth set you free?**

Of course, Wally isn't naïve. He knows that things happen in lives that are outside our control. He knows that illness, accidents, economic downturns and more can dash our plans, cause irreparable harm and seriously impede our WOW! numbers' growth. But for most of us, the real challenge isn't circumstance, but rather our attitudes.

Look around and you can see what Wally means. There is no doubt we are living in some of the easiest times the world has ever seen. Almost all Americans today, at the very least, have food on the table, warm clothes to wear, and a solid roof over their heads. Instead of candles, we have electricity. Instead of washing our clothes by hand, we have washers and dryers. Instead of horses, we have cars (really nice cars with heaters, air conditioners, power locks and windows). We have cell phones, computers and PDAs to make our lives easier. We are not poor. Yet, many are still not happy. Is this because of circumstances? No, it's because of attitudes. **Specifically, it's about bad attitudes.**

Our bad attitudes spoil us. We work hard, so we think we should be able to have whatever we want. We expect that it is our right to indulge in the things we please. If we want to go out all the time, eat nice meals, have a few drinks … then we deserve that. Yes, it's okay to indulge from time-to-time. But sadly, most of us don't know when to quit these days. Spending has become an addiction. We live in perhaps the easiest times the world has ever known, yet we feel empty inside. We are spoiled.

Wally begs you to please not get caught up in the "poor me" spider's web of today's spoiled world. Bad attitudes have thrown our priorities off track.

We need to realign our priorities and remember
the things that are really important in life.

24

No doubt this can be difficult in America. We are constantly bombarded by advertising. The prevailing message from all forms of media is that you are nothing if you don't have the latest and greatest whatever. In the face of this deluge, Wally says, "Get a grip." Take time to reflect. **Keep things in perspective.**

The WOW! life isn't about getting whatever you want, whenever you want it. It's about responsibility, commitment and diligence. Wally wants you to succeed. By following his advice, and keeping a good attitude, you can live the WOW! life.

You can thrive in the WOW! life.

"Wally, you're my hero!"

Chapter 25
The Scavenger Hunt

Do you remember going on scavenger hunts? You know, where somebody comes up with a list of things to find? Whoever finds all the things on the list first wins. It's a lot of fun!

Wally Wow's scavenger hunt is a little different. Instead of getting a list from somebody else, you make your own. The things Wally wants you to look for are things around your house that you purchased on an impulse. These are all **"Need for the Now"** items, such as:

- An exercise machine you just had to have and then never used.
- A "big-as-your-house" speaker system that you never play at full volume.
- The infrared "night vision" video camera that never even sees the light of day.
- Clothes that were in style at the time but never did fit or feel right.
- A CD that you bought just to get that one hot song.
- DVDs you bought, watched once and never played again.
- The auto-timer bread machine you got tired of cleaning the first time you used it.

See how it works? These are all "Need for the Now" items that you never really "needed" at all. You bought them on impulse. You gave in to the **"Need for the Now."**

So are you ready to play? Here are the rules.

Rule # 1
Go through your house. Make a list of all the "Need for the Now" items.

Rule # 2
Write down the prices you paid for each "Need for the Now" item. Add up your total. $_____

Rule #3
Look at that number. Ask yourself why you spent so much on stuff you didn't need. **Ask yourself what kind of WOW! number this stuff could have turned into for your retirement!**

Wally knows this game can hurt. He knows that most people are guilty of buying "Need for the Now" items from time-to-time. But, Wally also knows it is never too late to learn.

If your scavenger hunt number is really big, don't get discouraged. Lick your wounds and move on. Understand the "Need for the Now." Avoid the trap. **Remember that WOW! numbers are worth a lot more than a momentary urge (especially when you see how impulse items end up on Wally's scavenger hunt list).**

Play the game right. Remember that
"No Need for the Now" equals unbelievable WOW!

As a "consolation prize" for playing this game, can you salvage any of these costs? Can you hold a garage sale? Can you sell these items on the Internet? Take the money you can salvage from these items and turn it into a WOW! number!

Chapter 26
Wally Wow's Final Thoughts

26

You just read "Wally Wow Proudly Presents...WOW! Your Money." By now, you know the truth. Saving for retirement does not have to be hard. It does not have to be complex.

The key is to find your WOW! numbers. Help them grow. Keep at it.

Remember, you are the CEO of your money. Don't give up just because you stumble. Keep going. Doing something is always better than doing nothing. Your progress doesn't have to be huge every day. **When it comes to your WOW! numbers, small amounts, over time, add up to big results.**

Remember the attitudes of the financially wise. If you need reminders, **re-read this book. Refer to it often. Continue to educate yourself.**

The truth is you really didn't have to read the whole book. Everything you need to know about how to retire as a millionaire can be written on one page. That's right. You can retire with millions of dollars by following a simple formula for success.

Of course, Wally wrote a whole book on the subject. He did this in order to give you many examples. He wanted you to see how many ways there are to succeed. But the whole book can be summed up in a simple recipe for success.

Here is all that you need to do:

1. Invest in a proven mutual or index fund, with a balanced portfolio of bonds and money market funds in your 401(k)/IRA.
2. Buy a house that is affordable for you.
3. Pay off your mortgage by the time you retire.
4. Eliminate debts and other expenses by the time you retire (auto loans, credit cards, etc.).
5. Keep adequate health, auto, home and life insurance.
6. Maintain a savings account to cover emergencies.

That's all that you need to do. It is not complex. It is that easy. Follow that formula and you can retire a millionaire.

P.S. We'd love to hear how your WOW! numbers are growing. Send us your own WOW! number updates to mystory@wallywow.com Select stories will be published on our website, and may be selected as case studies for future books.

Chapter 27
A Message From the Authors

We are not accountants and/or financial planners. We are just average Joes like you! Hopefully we brought "Financing 101" to you in a different way than the traditional manner.

This book was designed with the character "Wally Wow" for several reasons. Wally Wow took on the image of a friendly financial superhero so we could explain to you in a third person, non-intimidating way how anyone, regardless of income or age, could truly retire better than they ever thought possible.

27

We opted to write this book in this manner and format. It was truly with a design in mind. The design is truly to WOW! you with **numbers to "WOW! Your Money."**

It is our hope that we inspired you to make some minor adjustments (major would be better) to take your money further than you ever thought possible. Starting with the Wally Wow 30 and creating your own new list and by "Shifting Your Spending" and "Grabbing the Cash" you are off to a great start! "Your Own Personal Gold Mind" is in you!

At the end of the day, end of the month, end of the year, your retirement is all about you being the CEO of your money. Wally wants you to become the CEO of your money and is giving you guidelines, but if you want to think outside the box, go for it. **Be creative and get involved in your finances, but do not forget to thank Wally Wow and "WOW! Your Money" for being your financial motivator.**

At times you may have questioned or disagreed with Wally, but we hope Wally Wow at least made you rethink some of your spending habits. We hope you will never look at a soda/snack vending machine the same again and that you will "Shift Your Spending." We hope you will enjoy being the CEO and managing your finances like a well-run business.

Our goal is truly that Wally Wow and "WOW! Your Money" will motivate you to begin your own financial planning with "Your Own Personal Gold Mind" one dollar at a time. When you retire, we want you to be able to say, **"WOW! I did not miss those few dollars a day, but what a WOW! retirement Wally Wow and "WOW! Your Money" gave me."**

If we brought one idea or many ideas to you, then the book was a huge success for us.

Wally Wow says **thank you very much** for purchasing and reading "Wally Wow Proudly Presents...WOW! Your Money."

Wally Wow wants to thank his staff!!!
Ryan Rath and Curt Rath (son and father team)... authors and creators.
Kim Rath (sister/daughter)... the idea of a Superhero, editing and proofreading.
Deb Rath (mother/wife)... editing, proofreading, and much patience.

A special thanks to Mike Reed, co-editor and everyone at TDI Print Graphics.

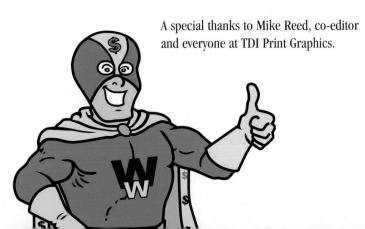